Beneath the

CW00549794

Understanding the Layers of Psychological Stress

By
William J. Lowry

DISCLAIMER

Copyright @ By William J. Lowry
2023. All rights reserved.

Introduction

Stress is a natural response to challenges or threats, whether real or perceived. Psychological stress refers to the emotional and physiological reactions that occur when an individual perceives a situation as challenging, overwhelming, or threatening.

Chapter 1

Types of Stress

Acute Stress

Acute stress is a type of stress that arises in response to a specific event or situation, typically one that is perceived as an immediate threat or challenge. This type of stress is a normal and adaptive physiological response designed to help individuals deal with potentially dangerous situations. Here are key features and aspects of acute stress:

1. **Nature of Acute Stress:**
   - Acute stress is short-term and is often linked to a specific incident or demand. It can occur suddenly and is typically resolved once the stressor is no longer present or the situation is resolved.

2. **Triggering Events:**
   - Acute stress can be triggered by a wide range of events, including:
     - A sudden danger or threat
     - A time-sensitive task or deadline
     - Unexpected challenges or obstacles
     - Intense emotional experiences, such as an argument or a surprise

3. **Physiological Response:**
   - The body's response to acute stress is part of the "fight or flight" mechanism. This involves the release of stress hormones like cortisol and adrenaline, leading to physiological changes such as increased heart rate, heightened alertness, and a boost in energy.

4. **Adaptive Function:**
   - Acute stress is considered adaptive because it prepares the body to respond quickly and effectively to a perceived threat. This response can improve the

chances of survival in a dangerous situation.

5. **Intensity and Duration:**
   - Acute stress is intense but short-lived. It is not meant to be a prolonged state, and the body is designed to return to a state of balance (homeostasis) once the stressor has been addressed or removed.

6. **Coping Strategies:**
   - Individuals may employ various coping strategies to deal with acute stress, such as problem-solving, seeking social support, or using relaxation techniques. Effective coping can help mitigate the negative impact of acute stress.

7. **Examples of Acute Stressors:**
   - Job interviews
   - Public speaking
   - Near-miss accidents
   - Sudden financial setbacks
   - Arguments or conflicts
   - Taking an exam

8. **Impact on Health:**
   - While acute stress is a normal part of life, chronic exposure to frequent acute stressors without adequate recovery can contribute to negative health effects. Prolonged activation of the stress response system may be associated with increased risk for certain health issues.

9. **Resilience and Individual Differences:**
   - Individual differences, including personality, coping skills, and resilience, play a role in how people respond to acute stress. Some individuals may be more resilient and better able to cope with short-

term stressors.

10. **Transition to Chronic Stress:**
    ○ If stressors persist or if there is a constant influx of
      new stressors without sufficient recovery, acute stress
      can contribute to chronic stress, which may have
      more lasting effects on physical and mental health.

Understanding acute stress and developing effective coping
mechanisms are essential for maintaining overall well-being, as acute
stress is a common and natural aspect of the human experience.

Chronic Stress

Chronic stress is a prolonged and ongoing state of stress that
persists over an extended period, often for weeks, months, or even
years. Unlike acute stress, which is a short-term response to an
immediate threat or challenge, chronic stress is characterized by a
continuous and sustained activation of the body's stress response
system. Here are key features and considerations regarding chronic
stress:

1. **Persistent Activation of Stress Response:**
   ○ Chronic stress involves a prolonged and repeated
     activation of the physiological stress response,
     including the release of stress hormones like cortisol
     and adrenaline.
2. **Causes of Chronic Stress:**
   ○ Chronic stress can result from a variety of sources, including:
     ▪ Long-term work-related pressures
     ▪ Ongoing financial difficulties
     ▪ Chronic health conditions or pain
     ▪ Relationship problems or conflicts
     ▪ Unresolved traumatic experiences

3. **Physical Health Impact:**
   - Prolonged exposure to stress hormones can have detrimental effects on physical health. Chronic stress has been linked to an increased risk of conditions such as cardiovascular disease, immune system suppression, digestive issues, and metabolic disorders.

4. **Mental Health Impact:**
   - Chronic stress is a significant risk factor for the development or exacerbation of mental health conditions, including anxiety disorders, depression, and burnout. It can also contribute to cognitive impairments and difficulty concentrating.

5. **Sleep Disturbances:**
   - Chronic stress is often associated with sleep disturbances, including difficulty falling asleep, staying asleep, or experiencing restorative sleep. Sleep problems, in turn, can exacerbate stress and contribute to a cycle of stress and sleep disruption.

6. **Behavioral Changes:**
   - Individuals experiencing chronic stress may adopt unhealthy coping mechanisms, such as overeating, substance abuse, or withdrawing from social activities. These behaviors can further impact physical and mental well-being.

7. **Impact on Relationships:**
   - Chronic stress can strain relationships, leading to increased conflicts and decreased emotional intimacy. Communication breakdowns and emotional exhaustion are common challenges.

8. **Workplace Implications:**
   - Persistent stress in the workplace, such as high job

demands, lack of control, or a toxic work environment, can contribute to chronic stress. This may result in decreased job satisfaction, productivity, and overall well-being.

9. **Individual Differences in Coping:**
   - Individual differences, including coping skills, resilience, and support systems, play a crucial role in how individuals manage and cope with chronic stress.

10. **Prevention and Management:**
    - Effective stress management strategies are essential for preventing chronic stress. This may include lifestyle changes, relaxation techniques, therapy, and seeking social support.

11. **Impact on the Brain:**
    - Chronic stress can affect the structure and function of the brain, particularly areas related to memory, learning, and emotional regulation. It may contribute to changes in neural pathways and increase the risk of neurological disorders.

12. **Risk of Burnout:**
    - Chronic stress, especially in the workplace, can contribute to burnout—a state of emotional, mental, and physical exhaustion often accompanied by feelings of cynicism and detachment from work.

Recognizing the signs of chronic stress and implementing effective stress management strategies are crucial for maintaining overall health and well-being. Seeking professional support, such as counseling or therapy, can be beneficial for individuals experiencing chronic stress.

Episodic Acute Stress

Episodic Acute Stress refers to a pattern where individuals frequently experience acute stress reactions. Unlike typical acute stress responses that are short-lived and tied to specific events, people with episodic acute stress tend to encounter repeated episodes of stress due to ongoing life situations or their personality and coping styles. This chronic pattern of acute stress can have various impacts on mental and physical health. Here are key features and considerations related to episodic acute stress:

1. **Frequent Acute Stress Episodes:**
   - Individuals with episodic acute stress often find themselves in a cycle of frequent and repeated acute stress reactions. These episodes may be triggered by specific situations or may arise from a general tendency to perceive many situations as stressful.

2. **Personality Factors:**
   - Certain personality traits, such as a predisposition towards anxiety, perfectionism, or a Type A personality, may contribute to the development of episodic acute stress.

3. **Lifestyle Factors:**
   - Chaotic and disorganized lifestyles, combined with a tendency to overcommit or take on too many responsibilities, can contribute to episodic acute stress.

4. **Highly Driven or Competitive Individuals:**
   - Individuals who are highly driven, competitive, or have an intense desire for success may find themselves in situations that trigger acute stress reactions due to the pressure they place on themselves.

5. **Worrying and Overthinking:**
   - Chronic worriers and individuals who tend to

overthink situations may experience episodic acute stress as a result of their constant anticipation of potential problems or threats.

6. **Impact on Health:**
   - The frequent activation of the stress response system in episodic acute stress can have negative effects on physical health. This includes an increased risk of cardiovascular problems, tension headaches, and other stress-related health issues.

7. **Relationship Strain:**
   - Episodic acute stress can strain interpersonal relationships, as individuals experiencing frequent stress may become irritable, impatient, or withdrawn.

8. **Workplace Implications:**
   - In the workplace, individuals with episodic acute stress may struggle with meeting deadlines, managing workloads, and collaborating with others. This can lead to decreased job satisfaction and performance.

9. **Treatment and Intervention:**
   - Recognizing the pattern of episodic acute stress is crucial for intervention. Treatment may involve stress management techniques, cognitive-behavioral therapy, and lifestyle changes to break the cycle of repeated stress episodes.

10. **Coping Strategies:**
    - Developing effective coping strategies is essential for individuals with episodic acute stress. This may include time management, setting realistic goals, learning to say no, and adopting healthier lifestyle habits.

11. **Role of Social Support:**
    ○ Social support from friends, family, or colleagues
      can be particularly important for individuals
      experiencing episodic acute stress. Having a
      supportive network can provide emotional
      assistance and practical help in managing stressors.

12. **Mindfulness and Relaxation Techniques:**
    ○ Practices such as mindfulness meditation, deep
      breathing exercises, and relaxation techniques can be
      beneficial in reducing the frequency and intensity of
      acute stress episodes.

Recognizing and addressing the underlying causes and patterns of
episodic acute stress is crucial for preventing its negative consequences
on health and well-being. Professional assistance, such as counseling or
therapy, may be valuable for individuals struggling with chronic stress
patterns.

Chapter 2

Causes of Stress

Work-related stress

Work-related stress is a common phenomenon that arises from the demands, pressures, and challenges individuals experience in the workplace. It can have significant implications for both mental and physical health, as well as organizational productivity. Here are key aspects and considerations related to work-related stress:

1. **Causes of Work-Related Stress:**
   - High workload, tight deadlines, and excessive job demands
   - Lack of control or autonomy in the workplace
   - Insufficient support from colleagues or superiors
   - Unclear job expectations or role ambiguity
   - Poor working conditions, including noise, lack of privacy, or uncomfortable physical environments
   - Job insecurity or fear of layoffs
   - Work-life imbalance and long working hours

2. **Physical Health Impact:**
   - Prolonged exposure to work-related stressors can contribute to physical health issues, such as cardiovascular problems, gastrointestinal disorders, and compromised immune function.

3. **Mental Health Impact:**
   - Work-related stress is a significant contributor to mental health conditions, including anxiety, depression, and burnout. It can also exacerbate pre-existing mental health issues.

4. **Burnout:**
   - Burnout is a state of chronic physical and emotional exhaustion, often accompanied by feelings of

cynicism and detachment from work. It is a common consequence of prolonged work-related stress.

5. **Effects on Job Performance:**
   - Work-related stress can lead to decreased job satisfaction, lower morale, decreased productivity, and an increased likelihood of errors or accidents on the job.

6. **Individual Differences:**
   - Different individuals may respond to work-related stressors in unique ways based on personality, coping styles, and resilience. Some may be more susceptible to stress, while others may handle similar situations more effectively.

7. **Role of Job Demand-Control Model:**
   - The job demand-control model suggests that stress levels are influenced by the combination of job demands and the level of control individuals have over their work. High demands and low control can contribute to increased stress.

8. **Workplace Culture:**
   - Organizational culture, including communication patterns, leadership styles, and the overall work environment, plays a significant role in the prevalence of work-related stress. A supportive and positive workplace culture can mitigate stress.

9. **Prevention and Intervention:**
   - Employers can implement stress prevention and intervention strategies, such as providing training on stress management, promoting work-life balance, and creating supportive work environments.

10. **Coping Strategies:**

- Individuals can adopt various coping strategies to manage work-related stress, including time management, setting realistic goals, seeking social support, and engaging in relaxation techniques.

11. **Workplace Policies and Programs:**
    - Organizations can implement policies and programs to address work-related stress, such as flexible work arrangements, employee assistance programs, and mental health initiatives.

12. **Legal and Ethical Considerations:**
    - Recognizing the potential legal and ethical implications, organizations are increasingly focused on creating work environments that prioritize employee well-being and comply with relevant regulations.

Addressing work-related stress requires a comprehensive approach that involves both individuals and organizations. Open communication, proactive stress management, and a supportive workplace culture are key elements in mitigating the negative impact of stress in the workplace.

Relationship stress

Relationship stress refers to the strain and tension that can arise within interpersonal relationships. It can affect relationships at various levels, including romantic partnerships, family dynamics, friendships, and professional relationships. Here are key aspects and considerations related to relationship stress:

1. **Causes of Relationship Stress:**
   - **Communication Issues:** Poor communication, misunderstandings, or lack of effective

communication strategies.

- **Conflict and Disagreements:** Differences in values, beliefs, or priorities leading to conflicts.
- **Financial Strain:** Money-related issues, such as financial difficulties or disagreements over financial decisions.
- **Unmet Expectations:** Unfulfilled expectations or unrealistic expectations about the relationship.
- **Infidelity:** Trust issues and emotional distress resulting from infidelity.
- **Life Transitions:** Stress arising from major life changes such as moving, job changes, or the birth of a child.
- **Lack of Intimacy:** Physical or emotional distance, leading to a lack of intimacy or connection.
- **Parenting Challenges:** Differences in parenting styles or disagreements about child-rearing practices.
- **Individual Stressors:** Stress from individual factors, such as work-related stress, mental health issues, or personal crises.

2. **Impact on Mental Health:**
   - Relationship stress can contribute to mental health issues such as anxiety and depression. It may also exacerbate existing mental health conditions.

3. **Physical Health Impact:**
   - Prolonged relationship stress can have physiological effects, including increased blood pressure, sleep disturbances, and a weakened immune system.

4. **Communication Breakdown:**
   - Effective communication is crucial in relationships,

and when it breaks down, it can lead to misunderstandings, resentment, and increased stress.

5. **Coping Mechanisms:**
   - Individuals and couples may adopt various coping mechanisms, such as seeking therapy, practicing active listening, and developing conflict resolution skills.

6. **Role of Support Systems:**
   - Support from friends, family, or professional counselors can be instrumental in helping individuals and couples navigate relationship stress.

7. **Relationship Satisfaction:**
   - Relationship stress can impact overall relationship satisfaction, leading to feelings of dissatisfaction or disillusionment.

8. **Relationship Resilience:**
   - Resilient relationships are better able to withstand stressors. Factors such as effective communication, mutual support, and shared problem-solving contribute to relationship resilience.

9. **Counseling and Therapy:**
   - Relationship counseling or therapy can provide a structured and supportive environment for couples or individuals to address and manage relationship stress.

10. **Preventive Measures:**
    - Proactive measures, such as regular communication, setting realistic expectations, and engaging in activities together, can prevent the buildup of relationship stress.

11. **Gender Differences:**
    - Men and women may experience and express

relationship stress differently. Understanding and acknowledging these differences can contribute to effective resolution.

12. **Time Management:**
   ◦ Balancing time between work, personal interests, and the relationship is crucial for preventing stress related to neglect or perceived neglect.

Addressing relationship stress requires open communication, mutual understanding, and a willingness to work together to overcome challenges. Seeking professional help when needed can be a valuable step toward resolving and managing relationship stress.

Financial stress

Financial stress is the emotional strain and anxiety that arises from financial problems or challenges. It can impact individuals and families at various income levels and can have significant implications for mental, emotional, and even physical well-being. Here are key aspects and considerations related to financial stress:

1. **Causes of Financial Stress:**
   ◦ **Debt:** High levels of debt, including credit card debt, student loans, or mortgages, can contribute to financial stress.
   ◦ **Job Loss or Insecurity:** The fear of losing a job or experiencing job insecurity can lead to financial uncertainty and stress.
   ◦ **Insufficient Income:** Not earning enough to cover basic needs and expenses can create financial strain.
   ◦ **Unexpected Expenses:** Sudden, unplanned expenses, such as medical bills or home repairs, can

disrupt financial stability.

- **Lack of Savings:** Insufficient savings to cover emergencies or unexpected events can contribute to stress.

- **Financial Dependence:** Relying on a single source of income or being financially dependent on others can create vulnerability.

- **Poor Financial Management:** Ineffective budgeting, overspending, or lack of financial planning can lead to stress.

- **Economic Factors:** Broader economic conditions, such as inflation, recession, or market fluctuations, can impact financial well-being.

2. **Impact on Mental Health:**
   - Financial stress is closely linked to mental health issues, including anxiety and depression. It can contribute to feelings of hopelessness and inadequacy.

3. **Physical Health Impact:**
   - Prolonged financial stress can lead to physical health problems such as headaches, sleep disturbances, and even cardiovascular issues.

4. **Relationship Strain:**
   - Financial stress can strain relationships, leading to conflicts, communication breakdowns, and even separation or divorce.

5. **Productivity and Work Performance:**
   - Employees experiencing financial stress may struggle with focus, productivity, and overall job performance.

6. **Coping Mechanisms:**

- Individuals may adopt various coping mechanisms, both positive and negative, to deal with financial stress. Healthy coping strategies include seeking financial advice, creating a budget, and building a support network.

7. **Financial Literacy:**
   - Improving financial literacy and understanding basic financial principles can empower individuals to make informed decisions and manage their finances more effectively.

8. **Social Stigma:**
   - There may be a social stigma associated with financial difficulties, leading individuals to avoid seeking help or discussing their financial challenges openly.

9. **Financial Counseling:**
   - Seeking the assistance of financial counselors or advisors can guide managing debt, budgeting, and planning for the future.

10. **Government and Community Resources:**
    - Utilizing available resources, such as government assistance programs or community support services, can provide temporary relief and assistance during challenging times.

11. **Long-Term Financial Planning:**
    - Developing and implementing a long-term financial plan can contribute to a sense of control and security, reducing financial stress over time.

12. ***Mindfulness and Stress Reduction Techniques:***
    - Mindfulness practices and stress reduction techniques, such as meditation and relaxation exercises, can help individuals manage the emotional

toll of financial stress.

Acknowledging financial stress and taking proactive steps to address it is crucial for overall well-being. Seeking professional advice, building financial resilience, and developing healthy financial habits are essential components of managing and overcoming financial stress.

Academic stress

Academic stress refers to the pressure and strain that students experience in educational settings. It can result from various factors related to the demands of academic life, including coursework, exams, deadlines, social dynamics, and future career expectations. Here are key aspects and considerations related to academic stress:

1. **High Workload:**
   - Heavy coursework, numerous assignments, and tight deadlines can contribute to academic stress. Students may feel overwhelmed by the volume of material to learn and the pressure to perform well.

2. **Exams and Performance Pressure:**
   - The fear of exams, performance evaluations, and the need to maintain high grades can create intense stress for students. High-stakes exams and standardized testing can add to this pressure.

3. **Time Management Challenges:**
   - Balancing academic responsibilities with other aspects of life, such as work, family, and social activities, can be challenging and contribute to stress.

4. **Perfectionism:**
   - Students who set extremely high standards for themselves may experience stress due to the constant pursuit of perfection and fear of failure.

5. **Transition Periods:**

- Transitioning to new academic levels (e.g., moving from high school to college) can be stressful as students adapt to new environments, academic expectations, and social dynamics.

6. **Social Pressures:**
   - Peer relationships, social expectations, and the desire for acceptance can contribute to stress, especially for those who feel the need to balance social life with academic success.

7. **Future Career Concerns:**
   - The pressure to choose a career path, secure internships, and meet expectations for future employment can create anxiety about the future.

8. **Inadequate Support Systems:**
   - Lack of academic support, whether from teachers, mentors, or peers, can intensify stress. Feeling isolated or unsupported can be detrimental to a student's well-being.

9. **Comparison and Competition:**
   - Comparing oneself to peers and feeling the need to compete academically can lead to stress. Unrealistic expectations and the fear of falling behind can contribute to this pressure.

10. **Physical Health Impact:**
    - Academic stress can manifest physically, leading to symptoms such as headaches, fatigue, sleep disturbances, and compromised immune function.

11. **Mental Health Impact:**
    - Academic stress is a significant risk factor for mental health issues such as anxiety and depression. It can also contribute to burnout and feelings of hopelessness.

12. **Coping Mechanisms:**
    ○ Students may adopt various coping mechanisms, both adaptive and maladaptive, to manage academic stress. Effective coping strategies include seeking support, practicing time management, and maintaining a healthy lifestyle.

13. **Perceived Lack of Control:**
    ○ Feeling a lack of control over academic situations, such as exams or assignments, can contribute to stress. Empowering students with a sense of control and autonomy can be beneficial.

14. **Procrastination:**
    ○ Procrastination, a common stress response, can exacerbate academic challenges and contribute to a cycle of stress and avoidance.

15. **Support Services:**
    ○ Access to academic support services, counseling, and mental health resources on campus can be crucial for helping students navigate academic stress.

Addressing academic stress involves recognizing the factors contributing to stress and implementing effective strategies for managing workload, building resilience, and promoting overall well-being. Educational institutions and support networks play a vital role in creating environments that foster positive mental health and academic success.

Chapter 3

Coping Mechanisms

Problem-Focused Coping

Problem-focused coping is a type of coping strategy employed to directly address and manage the specific issues or stressors causing distress. This approach focuses on finding practical solutions, taking action, and actively dealing with the problem at hand. Here are key characteristics and considerations related to problem-focused coping:

1. **Identification of the Problem:**
   - The first step in problem-focused coping is to identify and define the problem causing stress. This involves understanding the nature of the issue and its underlying causes.

2. **Analyzing the Situation:**
   - Once the problem is identified, individuals engage in a rational analysis of the situation. This may include gathering information, considering possible solutions, and assessing the potential outcomes of different actions.

3. **Setting Clear Goals:**
   - Problem-focused coping involves setting specific, realistic, and achievable goals related to resolving or mitigating the problem. These goals provide a roadmap for taking action.

4. **Generating Alternative Solutions:**
   - Individuals using problem-focused coping actively generate multiple solutions to the problem. This may involve brainstorming, seeking advice, or considering different approaches to address the issue.

5. **Decision-Making:**

- After generating potential solutions, individuals make decisions about which course of action to pursue. This decision-making process is informed by the analysis of the situation and the evaluation of the potential effectiveness of each solution.

6. **Taking Action:**
   - Problem-focused coping emphasizes taking concrete steps to implement the chosen solution. This could involve initiating conversations, making changes to one's environment, or enacting specific behaviors to address the problem.

7. **Monitoring Progress:**
   - Individuals using problem-focused coping continually monitor and evaluate their progress in addressing the problem. This involves assessing whether the chosen solution is effective and making adjustments if necessary.

8. **Seeking Social Support:**
   - While problem-focused coping is an individual effort, seeking support from others can be an integral part of the process. This may involve collaborating with others to find solutions or seeking advice from friends, family, or colleagues.

9. **Effective Communication:**
   - Clear and effective communication is crucial in problem-focused coping. Communicating needs, expectations, and solutions facilitates collaboration and support from others.

10. **Time Management:**
    - Effectively managing time is an important aspect of problem-focused coping. Allocating time for problem-solving activities and breaking down tasks

into manageable steps can enhance efficiency.

11. **Applicability to Various Stressors:**
    ○ Problem-focused coping applies to a wide range of stressors, including academic challenges, work-related issues, relationship difficulties, and other life stressors.

12. **Adaptability:**
    ○ Problem-focused coping strategies can be adapted to different situations and contexts. The flexibility to adjust strategies based on the specific nature of the problem enhances their effectiveness.

Problem-focused coping is particularly beneficial in situations where individuals have a degree of control over the stressor and when finding a solution or taking action is feasible. However, it may be less effective in situations where the stressor is beyond an individual's control or when emotional processing and support are equally important. Combining problem-focused coping with emotion-focused coping can create a more comprehensive approach to stress management.

Emotion-focused coping

Emotion-focused coping is a type of coping strategy that involves managing the emotional distress associated with a stressful situation rather than directly addressing the problem itself. This approach aims to regulate and alleviate the emotional responses to stressors, especially when the stressor may be beyond an individual's control. Here are key characteristics and considerations related to emotion-focused coping:

1. **Acknowledging Emotions:**
   ○ Emotion-focused coping begins with recognizing and acknowledging one's emotional reactions to a

stressor. This involves understanding and accepting the feelings associated with the situation.

2. **Expression of Emotions:**
   - Expressing emotions is a key aspect of this coping strategy. This can include talking to others about one's feelings, writing in a journal, or engaging in creative outlets as a means of emotional expression.

3. **Distraction and Avoidance:**
   - Distraction techniques and avoidance may be employed to temporarily shift attention away from the stressor. This can involve engaging in activities that provide relief or divert attention from the source of stress.

4. **Mindfulness and Meditation:**
   - Practices such as mindfulness and meditation are commonly used in emotion-focused coping. These techniques help individuals stay present at the moment, observe their emotions without judgment, and cultivate a sense of calm.

5. **Seeking Social Support:**
   - Emotion-focused coping often involves seeking support from friends, family, or other social networks. Talking about emotions and receiving empathy and understanding can provide emotional relief.

6. **Cognitive Restructuring:**
   - Changing the way, one thinks about a stressful situation is a cognitive strategy within emotion-focused coping. This may involve reframing negative thoughts or challenging irrational beliefs that contribute to emotional distress.

7. **Self-Compassion:**

- ○ Being compassionate toward oneself during times of stress is an important component of emotion-focused coping. This includes treating oneself with kindness and understanding rather than self-criticism.

8. **Catharsis:**
   - ○ Engaging in activities that allow for emotional release, such as crying, yelling into a pillow, or participating in physical activities, can provide a sense of catharsis and emotional relief.

9. **Humor and Positive Distraction:**
   - ○ Using humor as a coping mechanism or engaging in activities that bring joy and positivity can help shift the emotional tone and provide a break from stressors.

10. **Acceptance:**
    - ○ Emotion-focused coping recognizes that certain stressors may be beyond an individual's control. Acceptance involves acknowledging the reality of the situation and finding ways to cope with the emotional consequences.

11. **Applicability to Chronic Stress:**
    - ○ Emotion-focused coping is often employed in situations where the stressor is persistent or when the individual cannot directly change the external circumstances contributing to stress.

12. **Integration with Problem-Focused Coping:**
    - ○ Emotion-focused coping is not mutually exclusive with problem-focused coping. A balanced approach often involves integrating both strategies based on the nature of the stressor.

Emotion-focused coping is valuable in situations where the stressor is uncontrollable or when immediate problem-solving is not feasible. While it may not directly address the root cause of the stress, it helps individuals manage their emotional responses and promotes psychological well-being. Depending on the context, a combination of both emotion-focused and problem-focused coping strategies can enhance overall resilience and adaptive functioning.

Avoidant coping

Avoidant coping is a type of coping strategy characterized by efforts to evade or escape dealing directly with a stressor or an emotionally distressing situation. Instead of confronting the problem or seeking a solution, individuals using avoidant coping may employ various avoidance mechanisms to manage their emotions and reduce immediate discomfort. Here are key features and considerations related to avoidant coping:

1. **Avoidance Behaviors:**
   - Individuals engaging in avoidant coping actively avoid situations, people, or thoughts associated with the stressor. This can include physical avoidance, such as not attending events, as well as cognitive avoidance, such as suppressing thoughts related to the stressor.

2. **Denial:**
   - Denial is a common aspect of avoidant coping, where individuals may refuse to acknowledge the existence or severity of the stressor. This can be a defense mechanism to shield oneself from the emotional impact of the situation.

3. **Distraction:**
   - Distraction involves redirecting attention away from

the stressor through activities or behaviors that provide temporary relief. This can include engaging in hobbies, excessive use of entertainment, or overcommitting to work to avoid facing the stressor.

4. **Substance Use:**
    ○ Some individuals may turn to substances such as alcohol, drugs, or other addictive behaviors to numb emotions and avoid confronting the stressor. This can be a maladaptive form of avoidant coping.

5. **Procrastination:**
    ○ Procrastination is a common avoidant coping strategy where individuals delay taking action or making decisions related to the stressor. This delay may provide short-term relief but can lead to increased stress in the long run.

6. **Social Withdrawal:**
    ○ Avoidant coping may involve withdrawing from social interactions and isolating oneself from others to minimize the potential for emotional discomfort or confrontation.

7. **Escapism:**
    ○ Engaging in activities that provide an escape from reality, such as excessive use of television, video games, or daydreaming, is a form of avoidant coping.

8. **Minimization:**
    ○ Minimization involves downplaying the significance of the stressor or convincing oneself that the situation is not as serious as it may be. This cognitive distortion can be a way to reduce emotional distress.

9. **Compartmentalization:**
    ○ Compartmentalization is a mental strategy where individuals separate aspects of their lives to avoid

dealing with conflicting emotions. This allows them to focus on one area while avoiding the stressor in another.

10. **Short-Term Relief, Long-Term Consequences:**
    - While avoidant coping may provide temporary relief from emotional distress, it often comes at the cost of long-term consequences. Unresolved stressors can persist and lead to increased difficulties over time.

11. **Negative Impact on Mental Health:**
    - Relying heavily on avoidant coping can contribute to heightened anxiety, depression, and other mental health issues. It may hinder personal growth and problem-solving skills.

12. **Cycle of Avoidance:**
    - Engaging in avoidant coping can create a cycle where the stressor remains unaddressed, leading to increased anxiety and a reliance on avoidance as a primary coping mechanism.

Understanding avoidant coping is crucial because, while it may provide temporary relief, it does not address the underlying issues or contribute to long-term well-being. Encouraging individuals to develop more adaptive coping strategies, such as problem-focused or emotion-focused coping, can be beneficial in fostering resilience and growth in the face of stressors.

Chapter 4

Physiological Impact

Effects of stress on the immune system

Stress can have significant effects on the immune system, potentially impacting its function and responsiveness. The relationship between stress and the immune system is complex, and various mechanisms come into play. Here are some key ways in which stress can affect the immune system:

1. **Release of Stress Hormones:**
   - When the body perceives stress, the hypothalamus-pituitary-adrenal (HPA) axis is activated, leading to the release of stress hormones, particularly cortisol. While cortisol is important for short-term stress responses, prolonged or chronic stress can result in sustained elevated cortisol levels, which may suppress certain immune functions.

2. **Impact on Immune Cells:**
   - Chronic stress has been associated with changes in the number and function of immune cells. For example, prolonged stress can lead to a decrease in the number of lymphocytes (white blood cells critical for immune response), particularly T cells and natural killer (NK) cells.

3. **Inflammation:**
   - Chronic stress may contribute to a state of chronic low-grade inflammation. Inflammation is a normal part of the immune response, but prolonged or excessive inflammation can be harmful. Stress-related inflammation is linked to various health conditions, including autoimmune disorders and chronic diseases.

4. **Suppression of Immune Response:**
   - Chronic stress has been shown to suppress the immune response to some extent, making individuals more susceptible to infections. This suppression can affect both the innate and adaptive immune systems, reducing the body's ability to defend against pathogens.
5. **Altered Cytokine Production:**
   - Cytokines are signaling molecules that play a crucial role in immune system communication. Chronic stress can alter the production and balance of cytokines, contributing to dysregulation in the immune response.
6. **Delayed Wound Healing:**
   - Stress can influence the process of wound healing. Chronic stress has been associated with delayed wound healing, possibly due to its impact on immune cells and the inflammatory response.
7. **Changes in Antibody Production:**
   - Stress can affect the production of antibodies, which are crucial for recognizing and neutralizing pathogens. Prolonged stress may alter the balance of different types of antibodies, potentially impacting immune defense mechanisms.
8. **Gut-Immune System Connection:**
   - There is a close connection between the gut and the immune system. Stress can disrupt the balance of the gut microbiota and increase intestinal permeability, potentially leading to immune system dysregulation.
9. **Individual Differences:**
   - Individual differences, including genetic factors, resilience, and coping mechanisms, play a role in

how individuals respond to stress and how their immune systems are affected.

10. **Contribution to Chronic Diseases:**
    - Chronic stress and its associated impact on the immune system have been linked to an increased risk of developing chronic diseases, including cardiovascular disease, autoimmune disorders, and inflammatory conditions.

It's important to note that not all stress is detrimental, and short-term stress responses are a natural part of the body's adaptive mechanisms. However, chronic or persistent stress without adequate recovery can lead to long-term immune system dysregulation and negative health outcomes. Adopting stress management techniques, maintaining a healthy lifestyle, and seeking social support are important strategies for supporting immune system health in the face of stress.

Stress and cardiovascular health

Stress can have significant effects on cardiovascular health, contributing to the development and exacerbation of various cardiovascular conditions. The relationship between stress and the cardiovascular system is complex, involving both direct and indirect mechanisms. Here are key ways in which stress can impact cardiovascular health:

1. **Activation of the Sympathetic Nervous System:**
    - Stress triggers the "fight or flight" response, leading to the activation of the sympathetic nervous system. This results in the release of stress hormones, such as adrenaline and cortisol, which can temporarily increase heart rate and blood pressure.

2. **Elevated Blood Pressure:**
   - Chronic stress has been associated with prolonged elevation of blood pressure. Sustained high blood pressure (hypertension) is a significant risk factor for cardiovascular diseases, including heart attacks and strokes.

3. **Inflammation:**
   - Chronic stress can contribute to a state of chronic low-grade inflammation in the body. Inflammation is implicated in the development and progression of atherosclerosis, a condition characterized by the buildup of plaque in the arteries, leading to reduced blood flow.

4. **Impact on Cholesterol Levels:**
   - Stress may influence cholesterol levels. Some studies suggest that chronic stress can lead to unfavorable changes in lipid profiles, including increased levels of low-density lipoprotein (LDL or "bad" cholesterol) and decreased levels of high-density lipoprotein (HDL or "good" cholesterol).

5. **Blood Clotting and Thrombosis:**
   - Stress can affect the blood's clotting ability, making it more prone to forming clots. Increased blood clotting can contribute to the development of cardiovascular events, such as heart attacks and strokes.

6. **Insulin Resistance:**
   - Chronic stress has been associated with the development of insulin resistance, a condition in which the body's cells become less responsive to insulin. Insulin resistance is linked to an increased risk of type 2 diabetes and cardiovascular disease.

7. **Impact on Heart Rhythm:**
   - Stress can influence the electrical activity of the heart, potentially leading to arrhythmias (irregular heartbeats). Severe stress or acute stress events may trigger conditions like atrial fibrillation.

8. **Behavioral Factors:**
   - Stress can contribute to unhealthy behaviors that negatively impact cardiovascular health. Individuals under stress may be more likely to engage in smoking, overeating, or neglecting regular exercise, all of which are risk factors for cardiovascular diseases.

9. **Psychological Factors:**
   - Chronic stress is associated with psychological factors such as anxiety and depression. These conditions, when present, can independently contribute to cardiovascular risk and negatively affect overall well-being.

10. **Impact on Endothelial Function:**
    - Chronic stress may impair the function of the endothelium, the inner lining of blood vessels. Impaired endothelial function is a precursor to atherosclerosis and can contribute to vascular dysfunction.

11. **Contributor to Cardiovascular Events:**
    - Chronic stress has been identified as a potential contributor to acute cardiovascular events, including heart attacks and sudden cardiac events.

12. **Individual Variability:**
    - Individual responses to stress vary and some individuals may be more susceptible to the cardiovascular effects of stress than others. Factors

such as genetics, coping mechanisms, and resilience play a role.

Managing stress is crucial for cardiovascular health. Strategies for stress reduction, including regular exercise, relaxation techniques, mindfulness, social support, and healthy lifestyle habits, can positively impact the cardiovascular system and reduce the risk of cardiovascular diseases. Additionally, seeking professional support for stress management and addressing underlying psychological factors can be beneficial for overall well-being.

Psychosomatic disorders

Psychosomatic disorders, also known as psychophysiological or psychogenic disorders, refer to physical symptoms or illnesses that are believed to be caused or significantly influenced by psychological factors. These disorders involve an intricate interplay between the mind and body, where emotional or mental stressors contribute to the manifestation or exacerbation of physical symptoms. Here are key features and considerations related to psychosomatic disorders:

1. **Mind-Body Connection:**
   - Psychosomatic disorders emphasize the connection between mental and physical health. Emotional and psychological factors are thought to play a role in the onset, progression, or exacerbation of physical symptoms.
2. **Physical Symptoms without Clear Organic Basis:**
   - Psychosomatic disorders often involve physical symptoms that lack a clear organic or physiological basis. This can make diagnosis and treatment challenging, as there may not be easily identifiable structural or biochemical abnormalities.

3. **Stress as a Trigger:**
   - Stress is a common trigger for psychosomatic symptoms. Emotional stressors, traumatic experiences, or unresolved psychological conflicts may lead to the development or worsening of physical symptoms.
4. **Variety of Symptoms:**
   - Psychosomatic disorders can manifest with a wide range of physical symptoms, including pain, gastrointestinal issues, respiratory symptoms, neurological symptoms, and cardiovascular symptoms. Examples include tension headaches, irritable bowel syndrome (IBS), and certain skin disorders.
5. **Impact of Emotions on Symptoms:**
   - Emotional states, such as anxiety, depression, or unresolved anger, can influence the intensity and frequency of physical symptoms in psychosomatic disorders. Changes in emotional well-being may correlate with changes in physical symptoms.
6. **Somatization Disorder:**
   - Somatization disorder is a specific type of psychosomatic disorder characterized by the presence of multiple, recurring physical symptoms that cannot be explained by a medical condition. These symptoms often lead individuals to seek medical attention, resulting in a complex diagnostic process.
7. **Role of Personality and Coping Styles:**
   - Certain personality traits and coping styles may contribute to the development of psychosomatic disorders. Individuals with a tendency to internalize

stress, have difficulty expressing emotions, or struggle with coping mechanisms may be more susceptible.

8. **Chronic Nature:**
   - Psychosomatic disorders can be chronic, with symptoms persisting over an extended period. The chronicity often necessitates a comprehensive and multidisciplinary approach to treatment.

9. **Overlap with Other Mental Health Disorders:**
   - Psychosomatic disorders may coexist with other mental health disorders, such as anxiety disorders, depression, or post-traumatic stress disorder (PTSD). Addressing underlying psychological issues is essential for effective treatment.

10. **Biopsychosocial Model:**
    - The biopsychosocial model considers the complex interplay of biological, psychological, and social factors in the development of psychosomatic disorders. This model emphasizes the need for holistic and integrated approaches to assessment and intervention.

11. **Treatment Approaches:**
    - Treatment typically involves a combination of medical and psychological interventions. Medical management may focus on symptom relief, while psychological interventions, such as psychotherapy, stress management, and relaxation techniques, address underlying emotional factors.

12. **Collaboration between Medical and Mental Health Professionals:**
    - Collaborative care involving healthcare providers from various disciplines, including physicians,

psychologists, and other mental health professionals, is often crucial for the effective management of psychosomatic disorders.

Understanding the complex interplay between psychological and physical factors is key to diagnosing and treating psychosomatic disorders. A comprehensive approach that addresses both the emotional and physical aspects of the condition is generally the most effective way to manage these disorders and improve overall well-being.

Chapter 5

Psychological Impact

Anxiety disorders

Anxiety disorders are a group of mental health conditions characterized by excessive and persistent worry, fear, or apprehension. These feelings are often disproportionate to the actual situation and can interfere with daily functioning. Anxiety disorders are among the most common mental health disorders and can manifest in various forms. Here are some of the key types of anxiety disorders:

1. **Generalized Anxiety Disorder (GAD):**
   - GAD is characterized by persistent and excessive worry about various aspects of life, such as work, relationships, health, or daily activities. Individuals with GAD often find it challenging to control their worrying and may experience physical symptoms like restlessness, muscle tension, and difficulty concentrating.

2. **Panic Disorder:**
   - Panic disorder involves recurrent, unexpected panic attacks—intense episodes of fear accompanied by physical symptoms like rapid heart rate, sweating, trembling, and a sense of impending doom. Individuals with panic disorder often fear future attacks and may avoid situations that they believe could trigger an episode.

3. **Social Anxiety Disorder (Social Phobia):**
   - Social anxiety disorder is characterized by an intense fear of social or performance situations. Individuals with social anxiety fear being scrutinized or negatively evaluated by others. This fear can lead to avoidance of social situations, impacting

relationships, work, and daily activities.

4. **Specific Phobias:**
    ○ Specific phobias involve an intense and irrational fear of a specific object, situation, or activity. Common phobias include fear of heights, flying, animals, needles, or certain environments. Individuals with specific phobias may go to great lengths to avoid the feared stimulus.

5. **Obsessive-Compulsive Disorder (OCD):**
    ○ OCD is characterized by persistent and intrusive thoughts (obsessions) that lead to repetitive behaviors or mental acts (compulsions). Common obsessions include fears of contamination or harming others, while compulsions may involve rituals like handwashing, checking, or counting.

6. **Post-Traumatic Stress Disorder (PTSD):**
    ○ PTSD can develop after exposure to a traumatic event. Individuals with PTSD may experience intrusive memories, nightmares, and flashbacks related to the trauma. They may also exhibit avoidance behaviors, negative mood changes, and heightened arousal.

7. **Agoraphobia:**
    ○ Agoraphobia involves a fear of being in situations where escape might be difficult or where help may not be available. Individuals with agoraphobia may avoid crowded places, open spaces, or situations that trigger anxiety. It often coexists with panic disorder.

8. **Selective Mutism:**
    ○ Selective mutism is characterized by a consistent inability to speak in certain social situations despite the ability to speak in others. It often occurs in

children and may impact academic and social functioning.

9. **Separation Anxiety Disorder:**
    ○ Separation anxiety disorder is more commonly associated with children but can also occur in adults. It involves excessive fear or anxiety about separation from attachment figures, leading to distress when anticipating or experiencing separation.

10. **Unspecified Anxiety Disorder:**
    ○ Some individuals may experience symptoms of anxiety that do not fit neatly into one of the specific categories listed above. In such cases, a diagnosis of unspecified anxiety disorder may be given.

It's important to note that anxiety disorders can coexist with other mental health conditions, such as depression or substance use disorders. Effective treatment often involves a combination of psychotherapy, medication, and lifestyle changes. Early intervention and appropriate support are crucial for managing anxiety disorders and improving overall well-being. If you or someone you know is experiencing symptoms of an anxiety disorder, it is recommended to seek professional help from a mental health professional.

Depression

Depression, also known as major depressive disorder (MDD), is a common and serious mental health condition characterized by persistent feelings of sadness, worthlessness, and a lack of interest or pleasure in activities. It affects how a person thinks, feels, and handles daily activities. Depression is more than just feeling sad; it is a complex and multifaceted condition with various symptoms. Here are the key aspects of depression:

1. **Symptoms of Depression:**
   - **Persistent Sadness:** Feeling sad, empty, or having a depressed mood most of the day.
   - **Loss of Interest or Pleasure:** Losing interest or pleasure in activities once enjoyed.
   - **Changes in Appetite or Weight:** Significant changes in appetite or weight, either unintentional loss or gain.
   - **Sleep Disturbances:** Insomnia (difficulty sleeping) or hypersomnia (excessive sleeping).
   - **Fatigue or Loss of Energy:** Feeling consistently tired or having a lack of energy.
   - **Feelings of Worthlessness or Guilt:** Persistent negative thoughts about oneself, feelings of inadequacy, or excessive guilt.
   - **Difficulty Concentrating:** Trouble focusing, making decisions, or experiencing memory difficulties.
   - **Psychomotor Agitation or Retardation:** Observable restlessness or slowed movements and reactions.
   - **Suicidal Thoughts:** Thoughts of death suicide, or suicide attempts.

2. **Duration and Severity:**
   - To be diagnosed with depression, symptoms must persist for at least two weeks and significantly interfere with daily functioning. Depression can vary in severity, from mild to moderate to severe.

3. **Causes and Risk Factors:**
   - Depression is likely caused by a combination of

genetic, biological, environmental, and psychological factors. Trauma, family history of depression, certain medical conditions, and substance abuse can contribute to an increased risk.

4. **Types of Depression:**
   - **Major Depressive Disorder (MDD):** Characterized by the presence of significant depressive symptoms.
   - **Persistent Depressive Disorder (Dysthymia):** Involves chronic, long-term depressive symptoms that may not be as severe as MDD but can last for years.
   - **Bipolar Disorder (Depressive Episodes):** Alternating periods of depression and mania or hypomania.

5. **Treatment Options:**
   - **Psychotherapy (Counseling):** Cognitive-behavioral therapy (CBT), interpersonal therapy (IPT), and other therapeutic approaches can be effective in treating depression.
   - **Medication:** Antidepressant medications, such as selective serotonin reuptake inhibitors (SSRIs) or serotonin-norepinephrine reuptake inhibitors (SNRIs), may be prescribed.
   - **Electroconvulsive Therapy (ECT):** In severe cases or when other treatments haven't been effective, ECT may be considered.

6. **Support and Lifestyle Changes:**
   - **Social Support:** Building a strong support system through friends, family, or support groups can be

beneficial.

- **Physical Activity:** Regular exercise has been shown to have positive effects on mood and can be a helpful adjunct to treatment.
- **Healthy Lifestyle:** Maintaining a balanced diet, getting adequate sleep, and avoiding substance abuse contribute to overall well-being.

7. **Prevention and Early Intervention:**
   - Identifying and addressing depression in its early stages can prevent the worsening of symptoms. Early intervention often involves psychoeducation, support, and appropriate treatment.

8. **Professional Help:**
   - Seeking help from a mental health professional, such as a psychologist, psychiatrist, or counselor, is crucial for accurate diagnosis and treatment planning.

It's important to recognize that depression is a treatable condition, and with appropriate care, many individuals can experience significant improvement in their symptoms and quality of life. If you or someone you know is experiencing symptoms of depression, it's advisable to seek professional help as early as possible.

Post-traumatic stress disorder (PTSD)

Post-Traumatic Stress Disorder (PTSD) is a mental health condition that can develop in individuals who have experienced or witnessed a traumatic event. PTSD can have a profound impact on a person's emotional well-being and daily functioning. Here are the key aspects of PTSD:

1. **Traumatic Events:**
   - PTSD can result from exposure to a traumatic event or series of events that involve actual or threatened death, serious injury, or sexual violence. Common

triggers include military combat, sexual assault, natural disasters, accidents, and acts of terrorism.

2. **Symptoms:**

   ○ Symptoms of PTSD are generally grouped into four main categories:

      ▪ **Intrusive Memories:** Flashbacks, distressing dreams, or recurrent and involuntary memories of the traumatic event.

      ▪ **Avoidance:** Avoiding reminders of the traumatic event, including places, people, thoughts, or activities associated with the trauma.

      ▪ **Negative Changes in Thinking and Mood:** Persistent negative thoughts and feelings, distorted beliefs about oneself or others, persistent negative emotional states, and a reduced interest in activities.

      ▪ **Arousal and Reactivity:** Hypervigilance, irritability, difficulty concentrating, heightened startle response, and sleep disturbances.

3. **Duration of Symptoms:**

   ○ To be diagnosed with PTSD, symptoms must persist for at least one month and cause significant impairment in daily functioning. However, the onset of symptoms may not always occur immediately after the traumatic event.

4. **Acute Stress Disorder (ASD):**

   ○ In some cases, individuals may experience symptoms similar to PTSD in the immediate aftermath of a traumatic event. If these symptoms persist for at least three days but less than one month, the condition may be diagnosed as Acute Stress Disorder. If symptoms persist beyond one month, a diagnosis of PTSD may be considered.

5. **Risk Factors:**

   ○ Various factors can increase the risk of developing PTSD, including the severity of the trauma, a history of previous trauma, lack of social support, and pre-existing mental health conditions.

Individual differences in coping mechanisms and resilience also play a role.

6. **Impact on Daily Life:**
   - PTSD can significantly impact various aspects of daily life, including work, relationships, and overall quality of life. Individuals with PTSD may struggle with emotional regulation, experience difficulties in interpersonal relationships, and face challenges in maintaining employment or educational pursuits.

7. **Comorbidity:**
   - PTSD commonly coexists with other mental health conditions, including depression, anxiety disorders, and substance use disorders. Addressing these comorbid conditions is an important aspect of comprehensive treatment.

8. **Treatment Approaches:**
   - **Psychotherapy (Counseling):** Evidence-based therapies, such as cognitive-behavioral therapy (CBT) and eye movement desensitization and reprocessing (EMDR), are often effective in treating PTSD.
   - **Medication:** Antidepressants and anti-anxiety medications may be prescribed to help manage symptoms.
   - **Supportive Interventions:** Building a strong support system, participating in support groups, and engaging in self-care activities are essential components of treatment.

9. **Trauma-Informed Care:**
   - Trauma-informed care involves recognizing the impact of trauma on individuals and providing care

in a way that is sensitive to their experiences. This approach emphasizes safety, trustworthiness, choice, collaboration, and empowerment.

10. **Prevention:**
    ◦ Early intervention and support following a traumatic event can help prevent the development of PTSD. This may include crisis counseling, debriefing, and access to mental health resources.

PTSD is a serious mental health condition, but effective treatments are available. Seeking professional help from mental health professionals who specialize in trauma is crucial for accurate diagnosis and tailored treatment planning. If you or someone you know is experiencing symptoms of PTSD, reaching out to a mental health provider is an important step toward healing and recovery.

Chapter 6

Cognitive Aspects

Cognitive appraisal of stressors

Cognitive appraisal refers to the process by which individuals evaluate and interpret the significance of a particular situation or event. When it comes to stressors, cognitive appraisal plays a crucial role in determining how an individual perceives and responds to a given stressor. There are two primary stages of cognitive appraisal related to stress:

1. **Primary Appraisal:**
   - **Harm or Loss:** Individuals assess whether the situation or event has already caused harm or loss. If it has, the appraisal may lead to negative emotions like sadness or distress.
   - **Threat:** Individuals evaluate whether the situation poses a potential threat in the future. If so, it can lead to feelings of fear or anxiety.
   - **Challenge:** In some cases, individuals may perceive the situation as a challenge rather than a threat. This can lead to a more positive emotional response, such as feelings of excitement or motivation.
2. **Secondary Appraisal:**
   - **Coping Resources:** Individuals assess their available resources, including their coping skills, social support, and personal strengths, to determine how well they can manage or overcome the stressor.
   - **Control:** The perceived level of control an individual has over the situation is a critical factor. If individuals believe they have some control, they may

feel more empowered and capable of coping.

- **Future Outlook:** The assessment of the potential outcomes and implications of the situation influences the overall appraisal. A positive outlook may lead to a more adaptive response, while a negative outlook may contribute to increased stress.

Examples of Cognitive Appraisal in Stressful Situations:

1. **Job Loss:**
   - **Primary Appraisal:** Perceived as harm or loss if it has already occurred, or as a threat if anticipated.
   - **Secondary Appraisal:** Assessing coping resources, such as financial savings, support network, and employability. Control may be influenced by the perceived availability of new job opportunities.

2. **Exams in School:**
   - **Primary Appraisal:** Perceived as a challenge if viewed as an opportunity for learning and growth, or as a threat if seen as overwhelming.
   - **Secondary Appraisal:** Assessing coping resources, such as study habits, support from peers or teachers, and one's confidence in the ability to perform well.

3. **Relationship Conflict:**
   - **Primary Appraisal:** Perceived as harm or loss if there's already damage to the relationship, or as a threat if the conflict is ongoing.
   - **Secondary Appraisal:** Assessing coping resources, such as communication skills, emotional support, and the potential for resolution. Control may be influenced by one's perceived ability to contribute to

a resolution.

4. **Health Diagnosis:**

    ◦ **Primary Appraisal:** Perceived as harm or loss due to the impact on health, or as a threat if the diagnosis suggests potential future challenges.

    ◦ **Secondary Appraisal:** Assessing coping resources, such as access to medical care, emotional support, and personal resilience. Control may be influenced by the perceived ability to manage the condition.

Cognitive Reappraisal:

Cognitive appraisal is not a fixed process, and individuals can engage in cognitive reappraisal, which involves reevaluating the significance of a stressor based on new information or changing circumstances. Cognitive reappraisal can lead to a shift in the emotional and behavioral responses to stressors.

Understanding the role of cognitive appraisal in stress allows individuals to develop adaptive coping strategies, enhance resilience, and promote well-being. Techniques such as cognitive-behavioral therapy (CBT) often involve helping individuals reframe their thoughts and perceptions, contributing to more positive cognitive appraisals of stressors.

Cognitive restructuring in stress management

Cognitive restructuring, also known as cognitive reframing or cognitive therapy, is a therapeutic technique used in stress management and cognitive-behavioral therapy (CBT). It involves identifying and challenging negative thought patterns and replacing them with more positive and adaptive ways of thinking. The goal is to change irrational or distorted thought processes that contribute to stress, anxiety, or other negative emotions. Here's an overview of cognitive restructuring in stress management:

Steps in Cognitive Restructuring:

1. **Identify Negative Thoughts:**
   - The first step is to become aware of negative thoughts associated with a particular stressor. These thoughts are often automatic and may contribute to feelings of distress.

2. **Examine Evidence:**
   - Evaluate the evidence supporting and contradicting the negative thoughts. Are there facts or evidence that challenge the validity of these thoughts?

3. **Challenge Distorted Thinking:**
   - Identify and challenge cognitive distortions or irrational thought patterns. Common cognitive distortions include:
     - **Catastrophizing:** Assuming the worst-case scenario will happen.
     - **All-or-Nothing Thinking:** Seeing situations in black-and-white terms with no middle ground.
     - **Overgeneralization:** Making broad, negative conclusions based on a single incident.

4. **Generate Alternative Thoughts:**
   - Create more balanced and realistic thoughts that take into account a broader perspective. These alternative thoughts should be more positive, rational, and supportive.

5. **Practice and Repeat:**
   - Regularly practice replacing negative thoughts with more adaptive ones. Repetition helps reinforce the new thought patterns and makes them more automatic.

Example of Cognitive Restructuring:

Negative Thought: "I'll never be able to complete this project on time. I'm going to fail, and everyone will think I'm incompetent."

Cognitive Restructuring:

1. **Identify Negative Thought:** "I'll never be able to complete this project on time. I'm going to fail, and everyone will think I'm incompetent."
2. **Examine Evidence:** "Have I ever completed similar projects in the past? What skills and resources do I have to help me succeed?"
3. **Challenge Distorted Thinking:** "Am I catastrophizing by assuming failure? Are there more realistic outcomes? Is it fair to label myself as incompetent based on one project?"
4. **Generate Alternative Thoughts:** "I have completed projects before. I can break down the tasks, seek help if needed, and manage my time effectively. It's normal to face challenges, and it doesn't define my overall competence."
5. **Practice and Repeat:** Whenever the negative thought arises, consciously replace it with a more balanced and positive alternative thought. Over time, this new thought pattern becomes more automatic.

Benefits of Cognitive Restructuring in Stress Management:

1. **Increased Self-Awareness:** Cognitive restructuring encourages individuals to become aware of their thought patterns and the impact of those thoughts on their emotions.
2. **Improved Emotional Regulation:** By challenging and reframing negative thoughts, individuals can better manage and regulate their emotional responses to stressors.
3. **Enhanced Problem-Solving:** Cognitive restructuring promotes a more rational and solution-focused approach to problems, enabling individuals to identify and implement effective solutions.

4. **Reduced Anxiety and Depression:** Addressing distorted thinking can contribute to a reduction in symptoms of anxiety and depression, improving overall mental well-being.
5. **Greater Resilience:** Developing the ability to reframe negative thoughts enhances resilience, allowing individuals to cope more effectively with life's challenges.

Cognitive restructuring is often a component of broader cognitive-behavioral therapy (CBT) and is effective in helping individuals break the cycle of negative thinking and manage stress more adaptively. Working with a mental health professional can provide personalized guidance and support in learning and applying cognitive restructuring techniques.

Chapter 7

Individual Differences

Individual differences refer to the variations in characteristics, traits, and behaviors that distinguish one person from another. These differences can encompass a wide range of factors, including personality traits, cognitive abilities, emotional patterns, physical characteristics, and more. Understanding individual differences is crucial in various fields, including psychology, education, business, and healthcare. Here are some key aspects of individual differences:

1. **Personality Traits:**
   - Individuals exhibit unique combinations of personality traits that influence their behavior, emotions, and interpersonal relationships. Personality traits, such as extraversion, agreeableness, conscientiousness, neuroticism, and openness, contribute to individual differences.

2. **Cognitive Abilities:**
   - Cognitive abilities refer to mental skills involved in tasks such as problem-solving, memory, attention, and learning. Individual differences in cognitive abilities can influence academic performance, career success, and overall intellectual functioning.

3. **Emotional Intelligence:**
   - Emotional intelligence encompasses the ability to recognize, understand, manage, and use one's own emotions as well as understand and influence the emotions of others. There are variations in emotional intelligence levels among individuals.

4. **Learning Styles:**
   - Learning styles represent the preferred ways individuals absorb, process, and retain information.

Some people may prefer visual learning, while others may learn better through auditory or kinesthetic methods.

5. **Motivation and Goal Orientation:**
   - Individuals differ in their motivational patterns and the goals they pursue. Some people are highly motivated by achievement, while others may be motivated by affiliation, power, or intrinsic factors.

6. **Communication Styles:**
   - Communication styles vary among individuals, influencing how they express themselves, interpret information, and engage in interpersonal interactions. These differences can impact relationships and collaboration.

7. **Cultural and Social Background:**
   - Cultural and social backgrounds contribute significantly to individual differences. Factors such as cultural values, beliefs, upbringing, and socioeconomic status shape a person's worldview and behavior.

8. **Interests and Hobbies:**
   - People have diverse interests and hobbies, reflecting their preferences, passions, and recreational activities. These differences contribute to the richness of human experiences and social interactions.

9. **Physical Characteristics:**
   - Physical attributes, such as height, weight, facial features, and health conditions, contribute to individual differences. These characteristics can influence how individuals are perceived and may impact aspects of their lives.

10. **Values and Beliefs:**
    - Individuals hold varying values, beliefs, and ethical principles. These differences influence decision-making, moral judgments, and choices in personal and professional contexts.
11. **Attitudes Toward Change:**
    - Some individuals embrace change and novelty, while others may resist or feel uncomfortable with it. Attitudes toward change can impact how individuals adapt to new situations and challenges.
12. **Stress Coping Styles:**
    - Individuals exhibit different approaches to coping with stress. Some people may use problem-solving strategies, while others may rely on emotional expression or avoidance.
13. **Genetic and Biological Factors:**
    - Genetic and biological factors contribute to individual differences in traits such as intelligence, temperament, and susceptibility to certain health conditions.

Understanding and respecting individual differences is essential for creating inclusive and supportive environments in various settings. Recognizing and appreciating diversity contributes to effective communication, collaboration, and the promotion of equality and well-being. In fields like education and psychology, acknowledging individual differences is crucial for tailoring interventions and support to meet the unique needs of each person.

Chapter 8

Occupational Stress

Occupational stress, often referred to as work-related stress, is a complex and multifaceted phenomenon that arises when the demands of a job exceed an individual's ability to cope. It can have various sources and manifestations, impacting both mental and physical well-being. Here are key aspects of occupational stress:

1. **Causes of Occupational Stress:**
   - **Workload:** Excessive workload, tight deadlines, and high job demands can contribute to stress.
   - **Lack of Control:** Limited control or autonomy in decision-making and work processes can be stressors.
   - **Role Ambiguity:** Unclear job expectations and roles can create stress for employees.
   - **Interpersonal Conflicts:** Conflicts with colleagues or supervisors can contribute to workplace stress.
   - **Job Insecurity:** Concerns about job stability and future employment can be a significant stressor.
   - **Lack of Support:** Insufficient social support from colleagues or supervisors can increase stress levels.
   - **Organizational Change:** Rapid changes, restructuring, or uncertainty within an organization can be stressful.
   - **Inadequate Resources:** Insufficient resources, such as equipment or training, can contribute to stress.
   - **Shift Work and Irregular Hours:** Irregular work hours, night shifts, and long working hours can impact well-being.
   - **Work-Life Imbalance:** Difficulty balancing work

and personal life commitments can contribute to stress.

2. **Physical Health Consequences:**
   - Occupational stress is associated with various physical health issues, including cardiovascular problems, headaches, digestive issues, and musculoskeletal disorders.

3. **Mental Health Consequences:**
   - Chronic exposure to occupational stress can lead to mental health problems, including anxiety, depression, burnout, and increased risk of developing psychological disorders.

4. **Productivity and Performance:**
   - High levels of occupational stress can impair job performance, reduce productivity, and increase the likelihood of errors and accidents in the workplace.

5. **Absenteeism and Turnover:**
   - Employees experiencing significant stress may be more prone to absenteeism, and high levels of stress can contribute to increased turnover rates within organizations.

6. **Job Satisfaction:**
   - Job satisfaction tends to decrease when stress levels are high, negatively impacting the overall well-being of employees.

7. **Coping Mechanisms:**
   - Individuals may employ various coping mechanisms to manage occupational stress, including problem-solving, seeking social support, engaging in relaxation techniques, and setting boundaries between work and personal life.

8. **Workplace Culture:**

- ° The overall workplace culture, including the level of support, communication, and recognition, plays a significant role in determining the prevalence and impact of occupational stress.

9. **Prevention and Intervention:**
    - ° Organizations can implement strategies to prevent and manage occupational stress, including providing stress management training, promoting a healthy work-life balance, fostering a supportive work environment, and addressing sources of workplace stress.

10. **Individual Differences:**
    - ° Individual differences, such as personality traits, coping styles, and resilience, influence how individuals respond to occupational stress.

11. **Occupational Stress Assessment:**
    - ° Various tools and assessments are available to evaluate and measure occupational stress within organizations. These assessments can help identify specific stressors and guide interventions.

Addressing occupational stress requires a comprehensive approach that involves both individuals and organizations. Strategies to promote a healthy work environment, provide support systems, and enhance coping mechanisms can contribute to the well-being of employees and the overall success of the organization.

Chapter 9

Life Events and Stress

Life events, both positive and negative, can be significant sources of stress, influencing an individual's well-being and overall quality of life. The impact of these events on stress levels varies from person to person and is influenced by factors such as coping mechanisms, social support, and resilience. Here are some key aspects of life events and stress:

Types of Life Events:

1. **Major Life Events:**
   - Events such as marriage, divorce, childbirth, job loss, relocation, and retirement are considered major life events. These events often involve significant changes in roles, responsibilities, and daily routines.

2. **Daily Hassles:**
   - Daily hassles are ongoing, minor stressors that can accumulate and contribute to overall stress levels. Examples include traffic, financial concerns, work-related hassles, and interpersonal conflicts.

3. **Positive Life Events:**
   - Positive events, such as getting married, having a child, or receiving a promotion, can also be stressful. Positive life changes often require adaptation and may bring about new challenges and responsibilities.

4. **Negative Life Events:**
   - Negative life events, such as illness, loss of a loved one, financial difficulties, or relationship problems, are commonly associated with increased stress. These events can be emotionally and physically taxing.

Stress and Adaptation:

1. **Holmes and Rahe Stress Scale:**

- The Holmes and Rahe Stress Scale is a tool that assigns numerical values to various life events, allowing individuals to assess their cumulative stress level. Events such as marriage, divorce, and job changes are assigned scores, and the total score correlates with the risk of developing stress-related health issues.

2. **Individual Differences:**
   - Individual responses to life events vary based on factors such as personality, coping strategies, resilience, and the perceived level of control over the situation. What may be stressful for one person may not be as stressful for another.

Coping Mechanisms:

1. **Problem-Focused Coping:**
   - Individuals using problem-focused coping strategies address the practical aspects of a situation, taking steps to solve the problem causing stress. This approach is effective for controllable stressors.

2. **Emotion-Focused Coping:**
   - Emotion-focused coping involves managing the emotional response to stressors. This may include seeking social support, practicing relaxation techniques, or reframing thoughts to reduce emotional distress.

3. **Avoidant Coping:**
   - Some individuals may use avoidant coping, attempting to escape or ignore stressors. While this strategy can provide temporary relief, it may not be effective in the long term.

Impact on Health:

1. **Psychosomatic Effects:**
   - Chronic stress resulting from significant life events can contribute to psychosomatic effects, manifesting as physical symptoms such as headaches, digestive issues, and cardiovascular problems.
2. **Mental Health Impact:**
   - Prolonged exposure to stressors can contribute to mental health issues, including anxiety disorders, depression, and adjustment disorders.

Resilience and Social Support:

1. **Resilience:**
   - Resilience refers to an individual's ability to adapt and bounce back from adversity. Resilient individuals may navigate life events with greater ease and recover more quickly from stressors.
2. **Social Support:**
   - Having a strong support system can buffer the impact of life events on stress levels. Social support from friends, family, or colleagues provides emotional assistance and practical help during challenging times.

Life Event Assessment and Intervention:

1. **Assessment:**
   - Mental health professionals may assess the impact of life events on an individual's well-being through interviews, questionnaires, and other assessment tools.
2. **Intervention:**
   - Interventions may include counseling, therapy, stress management techniques, and support groups. These

approaches aim to help individuals cope with and adapt to the changes brought about by life events.

Understanding the interplay between life events and stress is crucial for promoting mental and physical well-being. Effective coping strategies, social support, and interventions can contribute to resilience and help individuals navigate the challenges associated with life changes.

Chapter 10

Social Support

Social support refers to the assistance, care, or comfort individuals receive from their social networks, including family, friends, colleagues, and community. This support can be emotional, instrumental (practical assistance), informational (advice or guidance), or appraisal-based (affirmation and feedback). Social support plays a crucial role in promoting mental and physical well-being and helping individuals cope with various stressors and challenges. Here are key aspects of social support:

Types of Social Support:

1. **Emotional Support:**
   - Emotional support involves providing comfort, empathy, and understanding during times of stress or emotional distress. It helps individuals feel valued and less alone in their struggles.

2. **Instrumental Support:**
   - Instrumental support includes tangible assistance or practical help. This may involve providing resources, assistance with tasks, or other forms of concrete aid.

3. **Informational Support:**
   - Informational support involves giving advice, guidance, or information to help individuals understand and navigate specific situations or challenges.

4. **Appraisal Support:**
   - Appraisal support involves offering feedback, affirmation, and constructive evaluation. It helps individuals gain perspective on their thoughts and feelings.

Sources of Social Support:

1. **Family:**
   - Family members often constitute a primary source of social support. Spouses, parents, siblings, and extended family members can offer a range of emotional and practical support.
2. **Friends:**
   - Close friends provide companionship, and understanding, and often serve as confidants. Friendships contribute significantly to emotional well-being.
3. **Colleagues and Peers:**
   - Supportive relationships in the workplace or academic settings can enhance well-being. Colleagues and peers may offer encouragement, assistance, and a sense of belonging.
4. **Community:**
   - Involvement in community groups, clubs, or religious organizations can provide a sense of community and social support. Shared values and interests can strengthen social bonds.
5. **Mental Health Professionals:**
   - Counselors, therapists, and support groups can offer specialized emotional and informational support to individuals facing mental health challenges.

Importance of Social Support:

1. **Stress Buffering:**
   - Social support acts as a buffer against the negative effects of stress. Having a strong support system can help individuals cope more effectively with life's challenges.
2. **Health Benefits:**

- Social support is associated with better physical health outcomes. It can positively impact immune function, cardiovascular health, and overall well-being.

3. **Emotional Well-Being:**
   - Strong social support is linked to greater emotional well-being, including lower rates of depression, anxiety, and feelings of isolation.

4. **Coping with Trauma:**
   - Social support is crucial for individuals coping with trauma, loss, or major life changes. It provides a sense of security and stability during difficult times.

5. **Enhanced Resilience:**
   - Social support contributes to resilience—the ability to bounce back from adversity. Knowing that one is not alone in facing challenges fosters a sense of strength and adaptability.

6. **Improved Coping Strategies:**
   - Individuals with strong social support may develop more effective coping strategies, as they can draw on the perspectives, advice, and experiences of others.

Challenges and Considerations:

1. **Quality vs. Quantity:**
   - The quality of social support is often more critical than the quantity. Having a few close, supportive relationships can be more beneficial than a large but less meaningful network.

2. **Cultural Differences:**
   - Cultural norms and expectations influence how individuals seek and receive social support. Cultural competence is important in understanding diverse

approaches to support.

3. **Changes in Relationships:**
   - Life changes, such as relocation, job changes, or family dynamics, can impact social support networks. Maintaining and adapting support systems is essential.

4. **Reciprocity:**
   - Social support is often reciprocal, with individuals providing and receiving assistance in turn. Building and maintaining relationships involve a give-and-take dynamic.

Seeking Social Support:

1. **Expressing Needs:**
   - Openly communicating needs and concerns helps others understand how they can provide effective support.

2. **Building and Nurturing Relationships:**
   - Actively investing in relationships, being available to others, and fostering a sense of trust contribute to a strong support network.

3. **Joining Supportive Communities:**
   - Engaging in communities or groups with shared interests or experiences can help individuals find like-minded individuals who can offer support.

4. **Professional Support:**
   - Seeking support from mental health professionals, such as therapists or counselors, can provide specialized guidance during challenging times.

Social support is a dynamic and evolving aspect of human relationships. Recognizing the importance of social connections and actively   cultivating   meaningful   connections   can   contribute significantly to individual well-being and resilience.

Chapter 11

Cultural Influences

Cultural influences encompass the impact of cultural values, beliefs, norms, customs, traditions, and practices on individuals and societies. Culture shapes various aspects of human life, including behavior, communication, identity, relationships, and worldview. Understanding cultural influences is crucial for promoting cultural competence, effective communication, and respectful interactions in diverse and multicultural settings. Here are key aspects of cultural influences:

1. Cultural Values and Beliefs:

- **Definition:** Cultural values are shared beliefs about what is important and desirable within a specific cultural group.
- **Influence:** Values shape individuals' priorities, decisions, and behaviors. They influence concepts of right and wrong, individualism vs. collectivism, and the importance of family, community, or personal achievement.

2. Cultural Norms:

- **Definition:** Cultural norms are accepted standards of behavior within a cultural group.
- **Influence:** Norms guide social interactions, etiquette, and expectations for appropriate conduct. They vary across cultures and impact how individuals express emotions, greet others, and engage in social activities.

3. Communication Styles:

- **Definition:** Cultural communication styles refer to the preferred ways of expressing and interpreting messages within a cultural context.
- **Influence:** Communication styles include verbal and nonverbal cues, levels of directness, use of silence, and attitudes toward eye contact. Cultural differences in communication styles can impact understanding and relationships.

4. Cultural Identity:

- **Definition:** Cultural identity is the sense of belonging and attachment to a particular cultural group.

- **Influence:** Cultural identity shapes how individuals perceive themselves and others. It includes aspects such as ethnicity, nationality, language, religion, and other affiliations that contribute to a person's self-concept.

5. Cultural Traditions and Practices:

- **Definition:** Cultural traditions and practices encompass rituals, ceremonies, celebrations, and customary behaviors within a cultural group.
- **Influence:** Traditions and practices reinforce cultural identity, provide a sense of continuity, and play a role in social cohesion. They can influence daily routines, lifecycle events, and community life.

6. Cultural Competence:

- **Definition:** Cultural competence is the ability to interact effectively with individuals from diverse cultural backgrounds.
- **Influence:** Culturally competent individuals understand and appreciate cultural differences, adapting their behavior and communication to be inclusive and respectful. It is essential in professions such as healthcare, education, and social services.

7. Collectivism vs. Individualism:

- **Definition:** Collectivism emphasizes group cohesion, interdependence, and loyalty, while individualism prioritizes personal autonomy, independence, and individual achievement.
- **Influence:** Cultural groups vary in the degree of collectivism or individualism. This influences social dynamics, decision-making processes, and the importance placed on group harmony vs. individual expression.

8. Time Orientation:

- **Definition:** Time orientation refers to the cultural approach to time, including whether the emphasis is on the past, present, or future.
- **Influence:** Cultures may be past-oriented, present-oriented, or future-oriented. These influence perceptions of punctuality, planning, and the importance of historical context.

9. Cultural Influences on Health and Well-being:

- **Influence:** Cultural factors influence health beliefs, practices, and attitudes toward illness and wellness.

Understanding cultural perspectives is essential in healthcare to provide effective and culturally sensitive care.

10. Cultural Diversity:

- **Definition:** Cultural diversity refers to the presence of various cultural groups within a society or community.
- **Influence:** Cultural diversity enriches societies by contributing a variety of perspectives, traditions, and experiences. It requires an appreciation for differences and the promotion of inclusivity.

11. Cultural Stereotypes and Bias:

- **Influence:** Cultural stereotypes and biases can shape perceptions, attitudes, and behaviors toward individuals from different cultural backgrounds. Addressing and challenging stereotypes is crucial for fostering understanding and reducing prejudice.

12. Globalization:

- **Influence:** Globalization has facilitated increased cultural exchange and interconnectivity. It influences the blending of cultures, the adoption of global norms, and the interconnectedness of societies.

13. Education and Cultural Learning:

- **Influence:** Cultural education and learning opportunities contribute to cross-cultural understanding, tolerance, and the development of cultural competence.

14. Intersectionality:

- **Influence:** Intersectionality recognizes that individuals hold multiple social identities (e.g., race, gender, socioeconomic status) that intersect and influence their experiences. Understanding these intersections is vital for addressing systemic inequalities.

Conclusion:

Cultural influences are dynamic and shape individuals and societies in multifaceted ways. Embracing cultural diversity, fostering cultural competence, and promoting open-mindedness contribute to positive intercultural interactions and a more inclusive and equitable global community.

Chapter 12

Mind-Body Techniques

Mind-body techniques involve practices that focus on the connection between the mind, emotions, and physical well-being. These techniques recognize the interplay between mental and physical health and aim to promote holistic well-being. Incorporating mind-body techniques into one's routine can help manage stress, enhance relaxation, and contribute to overall health. Here are some popular mind-body techniques:

1. Meditation:

- **Description:** Meditation involves cultivating a focused and calm state of mind. This can be achieved through various techniques, including mindfulness meditation, guided meditation, and transcendental meditation.
- **Benefits:** Reduced stress, improved concentration, enhanced self-awareness, and a sense of inner calm.

2. Yoga:

- **Description:** Yoga combines physical postures, breath control, and meditation to promote physical strength, flexibility, and mental well-being. Different styles of yoga exist, ranging from gentle and meditative to more vigorous and dynamic.
- **Benefits:** Stress reduction, improved flexibility, enhanced balance, and a sense of relaxation.

3. Tai Chi:

- **Description:** Tai Chi is a Chinese martial art characterized by slow, flowing movements and deep breathing. It emphasizes balance, coordination, and mindfulness.
- **Benefits:** Improved balance, reduced stress, increased flexibility, and enhanced overall physical well-being.

4. Breathwork:

- **Description:** Breathwork involves intentional control and manipulation of breathing patterns. Techniques can include deep diaphragmatic breathing, rhythmic breathing, and breath awareness.
- **Benefits:** Stress reduction, improved focus, enhanced relaxation, and promotion of emotional well-being.

5. Progressive Muscle Relaxation (PMR):

- **Description:** PMR involves systematically tensing and then relaxing different muscle groups in the body. This technique promotes relaxation and reduces muscle tension.
- **Benefits:** Stress reduction, relief from muscle tension, improved sleep, and enhanced overall relaxation.

6. Biofeedback:

- **Description:** Biofeedback is a technique that uses electronic monitoring to provide individuals with information about physiological processes such as heart rate, muscle tension, and skin temperature. Individuals learn to control these processes for health benefits.
- **Benefits:** Stress reduction, improved self-regulation of physiological responses, and enhanced well-being.

7. Guided Imagery:

- **Description:** Guided imagery involves using mental images or scenarios to evoke positive emotions and relaxation. It often accompanies deep breathing or meditation.
- **Benefits:** Stress reduction, enhanced focus, improved mood, and increased feelings of calm.

8. Mindfulness-Based Stress Reduction (MBSR):

- **Description:** MBSR is a structured program that combines mindfulness meditation and yoga to help individuals develop a mindful awareness of the present moment.
- **Benefits:** Stress reduction, improved emotional regulation, enhanced focus, and increased overall well-being.

9. Autogenic Training:

- **Description:** Autogenic training involves a series of self-statements that promote relaxation and stress reduction. These statements focus on sensations of warmth and heaviness in different parts of the body.
- **Benefits:** Stress reduction, relaxation, and improved well-being.

Chapter 13

Technology and Stress

Technology plays a significant role in modern life, offering numerous benefits such as improved communication, access to information, and increased efficiency. However, the use of technology can also contribute to stress, particularly when individuals struggle to manage the demands and potential downsides associated with digital devices and online activities. Here are some ways in which technology can impact stress levels:

1. Information Overload:

- **Issue:** Constant exposure to information through social media, news feeds, and email can lead to information overload.
- **Impact:** Feeling overwhelmed by excessive information can contribute to stress and make it challenging to focus on essential tasks.

2. Digital Connectivity:

- **Issue:** The constant connectivity facilitated by smartphones and other devices can blur the boundaries between work and personal life.
- **Impact:** Individuals may experience stress from the pressure to be constantly available, leading to difficulty in disconnecting and relaxing.

3. Social Media Comparison:

- **Issue:** Social media platforms often involve comparing one's life to others, contributing to feelings of inadequacy or fear of missing out (FOMO).
- **Impact:** Social media-induced stress can affect self-esteem and mental well-being.

4. Work-Related Stress:

- **Issue:** Remote work and the use of digital tools for work can lead to an "always-on" culture, blurring the boundaries between work and personal life.
- **Impact:** Persistent work-related demands can contribute to stress, burnout, and difficulties in maintaining a healthy work-life balance.

5. Cyberbullying:

- **Issue:** Online harassment and cyberbullying can lead to significant stress, anxiety, and emotional distress.
- **Impact:** Victims may experience mental health challenges as a result of negative online interactions.

6. Digital Addiction:

- **Issue:** Excessive use of digital devices, social media, or online activities can contribute to digital addiction.
- **Impact:** Addiction-related stress can result from difficulty in moderating screen time, impacting physical and mental well-being.

7. Fear of Missing Out (FOMO):

- **Issue:** Social media platforms often showcase others' experiences, leading to a fear of missing out on events or opportunities.
- **Impact:** FOMO can contribute to stress, anxiety, and a sense of social pressure to participate in various activities.

8. Digital Fatigue:

- **Issue:** Prolonged screen time and exposure to digital devices can lead to physical and mental fatigue.
- **Impact:** Digital fatigue may contribute to eye strain, headaches, and a sense of exhaustion, affecting overall well-being.

9. Economic Stress:

- **Issue:** The rapid evolution of technology can lead to job displacement, requiring individuals to adapt to new skills and industries.
- **Impact:** Economic stress may result from uncertainties about job security and the need for ongoing skill development.

Managing Technology-Induced Stress:

1. **Setting Boundaries:** Establish clear boundaries for device use, especially during non-working hours, to create a healthy work-life balance.
2. **Digital Detox:** Periodically disconnect from digital devices to reduce screen time and promote relaxation.

3. **Mindful Technology Use:** Practice mindful and intentional use of technology, focusing on its positive aspects and avoiding mindless scrolling.

4. **Balanced Screen Time:** Set limits on daily screen time, especially for recreational activities, to prevent digital fatigue.

5. **Tech-Free Zones:** Designate specific areas or times in your home where technology is not allowed to promote relaxation and family time.

6. **Regular Breaks:** Take breaks from technology, including short walks, stretching, or engaging in non-digital activities to refresh your mind.

7. **Cultivating Digital Literacy:** Develop skills to critically evaluate information and foster a healthy relationship with technology.

8. **Online Safety Measures:** Implement privacy settings, use secure passwords, and be cautious about sharing personal information online to reduce cybersecurity-related stress.

Balancing the benefits of technology with mindful and intentional use is key to managing potential stressors associated with the digital age. It involves cultivating a healthy relationship with technology and adopting strategies to promote well-being in both online and offline environments.

Chapter 14

Children and Adolescents

Children and adolescents, often collectively referred to as youth, represent a distinct demographic group with unique developmental needs, challenges, and opportunities. Understanding their physical, cognitive, emotional, and social development is crucial for providing appropriate support and guidance. Here are key considerations related to children and adolescents:

1. Physical Development:

- Children (Ages 0-12):
    - Rapid physical growth and development, including motor skills and coordination.
    - Milestones such as crawling, walking, and fine motor skill development (e.g., grasping objects).
- Adolescents (Ages 13-18):
    - Puberty and growth spurts leading to physical maturation.
    - Development of secondary sexual characteristics.

2. Cognitive Development:

- Children:
    - Rapid cognitive development, including language acquisition and problem-solving skills.
    - Concrete operational thinking, understanding cause and effect.
- Adolescents:
    - Development of abstract thinking and reasoning abilities.
    - Formation of identity, exploration of values, and future planning.

3. Emotional and Social Development:

- Children:
  - Formation of attachment and bonding with caregivers.
  - Developing empathy, emotional regulation, and social skills through play.
- Adolescents:
  - Formation of peer relationships and increased social influence.
  - Exploration of personal identity, autonomy, and independence.

4. Education and Learning:

- Children:
  - Focus on foundational skills, early literacy, and numeracy.
  - Play-based learning and exploration.
- Adolescents:
  - Formal education in middle and high school.
  - Increased emphasis on critical thinking, specialization, and career exploration.

5. Mental Health:

- Children:
  - Development of emotional resilience and coping skills.
  - Identification and support for early signs of mental health challenges.
- Adolescents:
  - Greater susceptibility to mental health issues like anxiety and depression.
  - Importance of open communication and destigmatizing mental health.

6. Parenting and Caregiving:

- Children:
  - Focus on providing a secure attachment, meeting basic needs, and fostering a supportive environment.
  - Parental guidance and supervision are crucial.
- Adolescents:
  - Balancing autonomy and guidance, supporting independence.
  - Open communication and understanding of adolescent needs.

7. Technology and Media:

- Children:
  - Limited exposure to age-appropriate media with parental guidance.
  - Emphasis on interactive and educational content.
- Adolescents:
  - Navigating digital spaces, social media, and online relationships.
  - Awareness of cyberbullying, digital literacy, and responsible technology use.

8. Risk-Taking Behavior:

- Children:
  - Exploration of the physical environment and mild risk-taking.
  - Need for supervision to ensure safety.
- Adolescents:
  - Experimentation with riskier behaviors, influenced by peer pressure.
  - Importance of education on healthy decision-making and risk assessment.

9. Nutrition and Physical Activity:

- Children:
  - Emphasis on balanced nutrition, age-appropriate portions, and active play.
- Adolescents:
  - Increased nutritional needs during growth spurts.
  - Encouragement of regular physical activity for overall health.

Chapter 15

Trauma and Stress

Trauma and stress are interconnected concepts that can have profound effects on an individual's mental, emotional, and physical well-being. While stress is a normal response to challenging situations, trauma refers to an overwhelming experience that can have lasting negative effects. Here's an overview of trauma, stress, and their implications:

Stress:

1. **Definition:**
   - Stress is a physiological and psychological response to perceived threats or challenges. It is the body's natural reaction to situations that require adaptation or coping.

2. **Types of Stress:**
   - **Acute Stress:** Short-term stress response to immediate challenges.
   - **Episodic Acute Stress:** Frequent acute stress episodes.
   - **Chronic Stress:** Prolonged stress due to ongoing situations.

3. **Sources of Stress:**
   - Stressors can be external (e.g., work demands, financial pressures) or internal (e.g., health concerns, relationship issues).
   - Perceived stress varies among individuals, and effective coping strategies play a role in mitigating its impact.

4. **Effects of Stress:**
   - Short-term stress can enhance performance (e.g., "fight or flight" response).
   - Chronic stress is associated with negative health

outcomes, including cardiovascular issues, mental health disorders, and weakened immune function.

5. **Coping Mechanisms:**
    ○ Coping strategies include problem-focused coping (addressing the stressor directly), emotion-focused coping (managing emotional response), and avoidant coping (trying to ignore or escape stressors).

Trauma:

1. **Definition:**
    ○ Trauma results from an event or series of events that are emotionally or physically harmful and have lasting adverse effects. Trauma overwhelms an individual's ability to cope.

2. **Types of Trauma:**
    ○ **Acute Trauma:** Resulting from a single event, such as an accident or natural disaster.
    ○ **Chronic Trauma:** Ongoing exposure to stressful events, such as domestic violence or prolonged abuse.
    ○ **Complex Trauma:** Multiple and prolonged traumatic experiences, often in interpersonal relationships.

3. **Causes of Trauma:**
    ○ Trauma can result from various events, including accidents, abuse, violence, natural disasters, and medical emergencies.

4. **Effects of Trauma:**
    ○ Trauma can impact mental health, leading to conditions such as post-traumatic stress disorder

(PTSD), anxiety, depression, and dissociation.

- Physical health issues, including chronic pain and autoimmune disorders, may be linked to trauma.

5. **Coping Mechanisms:**
   - Coping with trauma often requires therapeutic intervention, such as trauma-focused therapy, cognitive-behavioral therapy (CBT), and eye movement desensitization and reprocessing (EMDR).
   - Supportive relationships, social connections, and self-care are crucial for trauma recovery.

Connection Between Trauma and Stress:

1. **Traumatic Stress:**
   - Trauma induces a significant stress response, activating the body's fight-or-flight mechanism.
   - Traumatic stress can be acute or chronic, and the effects may extend well beyond the initial traumatic event.

2. **Complex Trauma:**
   - Complex trauma involves exposure to multiple and varied traumatic experiences over an extended period, leading to chronic stress responses.

3. **Impact on Coping:**
   - Individuals who have experienced trauma may develop maladaptive coping mechanisms, such as substance abuse or self-harming behaviors, to manage the overwhelming stress associated with trauma.

4. **Resilience and Recovery:**
   - Resilience, the ability to bounce back from adversity, plays a crucial role in trauma recovery.

- Trauma-informed care recognizes the impact of trauma on individuals and promotes supportive, empowering, and compassionate approaches.

Treatment and Support:

1. **Therapeutic Approaches:**
   - Trauma-focused therapies, such as exposure therapy, CBT, and dialectical behavior therapy (DBT), aim to address the psychological impact of trauma.
   - EMDR is specifically designed to process traumatic memories and reduce distress.
2. **Support Systems:**
   - Social support, including friends, family, and community, is essential for trauma recovery.
   - Support groups and peer support can provide a sense of understanding and connection.
3. **Self-Care:**
   - Self-care practices, including mindfulness, meditation, and physical activity, contribute to stress reduction and overall well-being.
4. **Professional Help:**
   - Seeking help from mental health professionals, including therapists, counselors, and psychiatrists, is crucial for trauma recovery.

Understanding the nuanced relationship between trauma and stress is essential for providing effective support and interventions. Trauma-informed approaches emphasize creating environments that prioritize safety, trust, collaboration, and empowerment to facilitate healing and recovery.

Chapter 16

Gender Differences in Stress

Gender differences in stress are influenced by a complex interplay of biological, psychological, and social factors. While stress is a universal experience, studies suggest that men and women may respond to and cope with stressors differently. Here are some key considerations regarding gender differences in stress:

1. Biological Factors:

- Hormonal Influence:
  - Hormones, such as cortisol and oxytocin, play a role in the stress response. Women may experience hormonal fluctuations related to the menstrual cycle and pregnancy, which can influence stress sensitivity.

2. Psychological Factors:

- Coping Styles:
  - Women often engage in more emotion-focused coping, seeking social support and expressing emotions. Men may be more prone to problem-focused coping, focusing on finding solutions to stressors.
- Rumination:
  - Women may be more likely to ruminate on stressors, dwelling on negative thoughts and feelings, which can contribute to prolonged stress. Men may be more inclined to distract themselves from stressors.

3. Social Factors:

- Social Roles and Expectations:
  - Societal expectations and gender roles can shape how individuals experience and express stress.

Traditional gender norms may influence the types of stressors considered acceptable for men and women.

○ For example, women may face stress related to caregiving responsibilities, work-life balance, or societal expectations related to appearance. Men may experience stress related to provider roles, career pressures, or expectations related to emotional expression.

4. Communication Styles:

- **Communication Patterns:**
  ○ Women may be more likely to seek emotional support and share their stressors with others. Men may be less inclined to openly express vulnerability and may internalize stress or discuss it less frequently.

5. Workplace Stress:

- **Workplace Challenges:**
  ○ Men and women may face different stressors in the workplace. For instance, women may experience stress related to gender bias, work-life balance, or discrimination. Men may face stress associated with competition, performance expectations, or job security concerns.

6. Health Impacts:

- **Physical Health Consequences:**
  ○ Chronic stress has been linked to various health issues, and there may be gender differences in how stress affects physical health. For instance, women may be more prone to stress-related conditions such

as autoimmune disorders, while men may be more susceptible to cardiovascular issues.

7. Life Transitions:

- Life Changes:
  - ○ Different life transitions, such as marriage, parenthood, or retirement, can elicit varying stress responses in men and women. Societal expectations and individual perceptions of these transitions may contribute to stress.

8. Trauma and PTSD:

- Trauma Response:
  - ○ Men and women may have different responses to trauma, and the prevalence of post-traumatic stress disorder (PTSD) can vary by gender. Women may be more likely to experience certain types of traumas, such as sexual assault, and may have higher rates of PTSD.

9. Social Support:

- Support Networks:
  - ○ Women often emphasize social support and maintain broader social networks, while men may rely more on a few close relationships. The quality and type of social support can influence how individuals cope with stress.

Chapter 17

Stress Assessment and Measurement

Assessing and measuring stress is a multidimensional process that involves evaluating various aspects of an individual's experience, including physiological, psychological, and behavioral responses to stressors. Several methods and tools are used to assess and measure stress in research, clinical settings, and self-report contexts. Here are some common approaches to stress assessment and measurement:

1. Physiological Measures:

- Heart Rate and Blood Pressure:
    - Monitoring changes in heart rate and blood pressure provides insights into the autonomic nervous system's response to stress.
- Cortisol Levels:
    - Cortisol, a stress hormone, can be measured in saliva, urine, or blood to assess the body's physiological stress response.
- Galvanic Skin Response (GSR):
    - GSR measures changes in skin conductance, reflecting sympathetic nervous system activity and emotional arousal.

2. Psychological and Self-Report Measures:

- Perceived Stress Scales:
    - Self-report scales, such as the Perceived Stress Scale (PSS), assess an individual's subjective experience of stress over a specified period.
- State-Trait Anxiety Inventory (STAI):
    - The STAI measures both temporary (state) and long-standing (trait) anxiety, providing insights into stress-related emotional states.

- Depression, Anxiety, and Stress Scales (DASS):
  - DASS is a self-report measure that assesses the severity of symptoms related to depression, anxiety, and stress.
- Stressful Life Events Scale:
  - This scale assesses the occurrence and impact of major life events that may contribute to stress.

3. Behavioral Observation:

- Behavioral Coding:
  - Observing and coding behaviors related to stress, such as facial expressions, body language, and verbal cues, provides qualitative data on stress responses.
- Task Performance:
  - Assessing changes in task performance and cognitive functioning under stress can provide behavioral indicators of stress.

4. Interviews and Clinical Assessment:

- Structured Clinical Interviews:
  - Clinicians may use structured interviews to assess stress-related symptoms and their impact on an individual's daily functioning.
- Diagnostic Criteria:
  - Assessing stress-related disorders, such as post-traumatic stress disorder (PTSD), involves evaluating symptoms based on diagnostic criteria.

5. Daily Diaries and Ecological Momentary Assessment (EMA):

- Daily Stress Diaries:
  - Individuals keep diaries to record daily stressors,

emotions, and coping strategies, providing a longitudinal perspective on stress.

- EMA Apps:
  ○ Smartphone applications can prompt users to report stress levels, allowing for real-time data collection in naturalistic settings.

6. Neuroimaging:

- Functional Magnetic Resonance Imaging (fMRI):
  ○ fMRI can assess brain activation patterns in response to stressors, providing insights into neural correlates of stress.
- Electroencephalography (EEG):
  ○ EEG measures electrical activity in the brain and can be used to assess changes in neural patterns associated with stress.

7. Stress Biomarkers:

- Inflammatory Markers:
  ○ Assessing levels of inflammatory markers, such as C-reactive protein, can indicate the body's response to chronic stress.
- Immune Function:
  ○ Measuring changes in immune system function provides information about the impact of stress on health.

Considerations and Challenges:

1. **Subjectivity:**
   ○ Stress assessment often involves subjective self-report, which may be influenced by individual perceptions and biases.

2. **Contextual Factors:**
   - The context in which stress is assessed (e.g., laboratory setting vs. real-world environment) can influence responses.
3. **Cultural Sensitivity:**
   - Cultural factors may impact the experience and expression of stress, necessitating culturally sensitive assessment tools.
4. **Temporal Dynamics:**
   - Stress is a dynamic process, and assessments may need to consider temporal changes and fluctuations.
5. **Multi-method Approach:**
   - Combining multiple assessment methods (physiological, psychological, behavioral) provides a comprehensive understanding of stress.
6. **Longitudinal Assessment:**
   - Longitudinal assessments allow for tracking changes in stress over time and capturing the impact of chronic stress.

Assessing stress is a dynamic and multifaceted process that often requires a combination of methods to provide a comprehensive understanding of an individual's stress experience. Clinicians, researchers, and individuals can select and integrate assessment tools based on their specific goals and the context of stress evaluation.

Chapter 18

Interventions and Treatments

Interventions and treatments for stress aim to help individuals manage and cope with the challenges and demands of life effectively. The choice of intervention often depends on the severity of stress, individual preferences, and the underlying causes. Here are various approaches to address and manage stress:

1. Lifestyle Changes:

- Exercise:
  - Regular physical activity has been shown to reduce stress by promoting the release of endorphins, improving mood, and providing a healthy outlet for tension.
- Healthy Diet:
  - Nutrient-rich diets contribute to overall well-being. Avoiding excessive caffeine, sugar, and processed foods can help stabilize energy levels and mood.
- Adequate Sleep:
  - Establishing healthy sleep patterns is crucial for stress management. Quality sleep supports cognitive function, emotional resilience, and physical health.

2. Mind-Body Practices:

- Meditation:
  - Mindfulness meditation, focused breathing, and guided imagery can promote relaxation, reduce anxiety, and enhance self-awareness.
- Yoga:
  - Combining physical postures, breath control, and meditation, yoga promotes flexibility, balance, and stress reduction.

- Tai Chi:
  - Slow, deliberate movements of tai chi can improve mental focus, reduce stress, and enhance overall well-being.

3. Counseling and Psychotherapy:

- Cognitive-behavioral therapy (CBT):
  - CBT helps individuals identify and change negative thought patterns and behaviors associated with stress. It is effective for various stress-related disorders.
- Mindfulness-Based Stress Reduction (MBSR):
  - MBSR combines mindfulness meditation and yoga to enhance awareness and reduce stress. It is often used in therapeutic settings.
- Talk Therapy:
  - Counseling provides a supportive space for individuals to discuss stressors, explore emotions, and develop coping strategies.

4. Relaxation Techniques:

- Progressive Muscle Relaxation (PMR):
  - PMR involves systematically tensing and relaxing muscle groups to release physical tension and promote relaxation.
- Deep Breathing Exercises:
  - Diaphragmatic breathing and other deep breathing exercises help activate the body's relaxation response, reducing stress.

5. Social Support:

- Connection with Others:

- ○ Building and maintaining strong social connections provide emotional support and create a sense of belonging, reducing the impact of stress.

- Support Groups:
  - ○ Joining support groups, whether in-person or online, can provide a sense of community and understanding.

6. Time Management:

- Prioritization and Planning:
  - ○ Effectively managing time, setting priorities, and planning daily activities can reduce feelings of overwhelm and increase a sense of control.

7. Crisis Intervention:

- Hotlines and Helplines:
  - ○ Crisis intervention services, such as helplines and crisis hotlines, offer immediate support for individuals experiencing acute stress or emotional distress.

8. Medication:

- Antidepressants and Anxiolytics:
  - ○ In some cases, medication may be prescribed to manage symptoms of stress-related disorders, such as depression or anxiety.

9. Stress Management Workshops:

- Educational Programs:
  - ○ Workshops and programs that teach stress management techniques, coping skills, and resilience-building strategies can be beneficial.

10. Biofeedback:

- Biofeedback Training:
  - ○ Biofeedback uses electronic monitoring to provide individuals with information about physiological processes (e.g., heart rate, muscle tension). It helps individuals learn to control these processes for stress reduction.

11. Holistic Approaches:

- Acupuncture:
  - ○ Acupuncture involves the insertion of thin needles into specific points on the body to promote balance and alleviate stress.
- Massage Therapy:
  - ○ Massage can reduce muscle tension, promote relaxation, and alleviate physical symptoms of stress.

12. Workplace Interventions:

- Employee Assistance Programs (EAPs):
  - ○ EAPs offer confidential counseling and support services for employees dealing with personal or work-related stress.
- Flexible Work Arrangements:
  - ○ Providing flexibility in work schedules and environments can contribute to a healthier work-life balance.

13. Assertiveness Training:

- Communication Skills:
  - ○ Learning assertiveness and effective communication skills can help individuals express their needs and boundaries, reducing interpersonal stress.

14. Journaling:

- Expressive Writing:
  - Journaling or expressive writing allows individuals to explore and process their thoughts and emotions related to stressors.

15. Nature and Outdoor Activities:

- Nature Walks and Outdoor Recreation:
  - Spending time in nature has been associated with stress reduction and improved mental well-being.

Considerations:

- Individualized Approach:
  - The effectiveness of interventions varies among individuals, and an individualized approach is often necessary.
- Combination of Strategies:
  - Combining multiple strategies may be more effective than relying on a single approach.
- Professional Guidance:
  - Seeking guidance from healthcare professionals or qualified practitioners can help individuals choose and implement appropriate interventions.

It's important to recognize that stress management is a dynamic process, and individuals may need to experiment with strategies to find what works best for them. Seeking support from healthcare professionals, therapists, or support groups can enhance the effectiveness of stress interventions.

Chapter 19

Prevention Strategies

Preventing stress involves adopting proactive strategies to manage life's demands, enhance resilience, and minimize the negative impact of stressors. Here are various prevention strategies that individuals can incorporate into their lives to promote overall well-being and resilience:

1. Healthy Lifestyle Habits:

- **Regular Exercise:**
    - Engaging in regular physical activity, such as walking, jogging, or yoga, helps release endorphins and reduces the physiological effects of stress.
- **Balanced Diet:**
    - Maintaining a nutritious and well-balanced diet supports overall physical and mental health, contributing to resilience against stress.
- **Adequate Sleep:**
    - Prioritize sufficient and quality sleep to optimize cognitive function, emotional well-being, and stress resilience.

2. Mind-Body Practices:

- **Mindfulness Meditation:**
    - Incorporating mindfulness meditation into daily routines can enhance awareness, reduce reactivity to stressors, and promote emotional regulation.
- **Yoga and Tai Chi:**
    - These practices combine physical movement, breath control, and mindfulness, fostering relaxation and stress resilience.

3. Stress Management Skills:

- Cognitive-Behavioral Techniques:
  - Learning and practicing cognitive-behavioral techniques can help individuals identify and reframe negative thought patterns associated with stress.
- Relaxation Techniques:
  - Regularly practicing relaxation techniques, such as deep breathing or progressive muscle relaxation, can alleviate tension and promote a sense of calm.

4. Time Management:

- Prioritization:
  - Develop effective time management skills by setting priorities, breaking tasks into manageable steps, and avoiding procrastination.
- Work-Life Balance:
  - Establish a healthy balance between work, personal life, and leisure activities to prevent burnout and chronic stress.

5. Social Connections:

- Maintain Relationships:
  - Cultivate and maintain strong social connections with friends, family, and community to provide a support system during challenging times.
- Open Communication:
  - Practice open communication with loved ones, expressing feelings and seeking support when needed.

6. Positive Lifestyle Choices:

- Limit Substance Use:
  - Avoid excessive use of alcohol, nicotine, or other

substances, as they can contribute to stress and negatively impact mental health.

- Healthy Coping Mechanisms:
  - Develop healthy coping mechanisms such as hobbies, creative activities, or relaxation techniques to manage stress.

7. Assertiveness and Boundaries:

- Effective Communication:
  - Learn assertiveness skills to express needs, set boundaries, and communicate effectively in various situations.
    - Say "No" When Necessary:
      - Recognize the importance of saying "no" when commitments or demands exceed one's capacity, preventing overwhelm.

8. Professional Development:

- Continuous Learning:
  - Engage in continuous learning and professional development to stay adaptive and enhance one's skills and confidence in facing challenges.
    - Seek Feedback:
      - Actively seek constructive feedback to foster personal and professional growth.

9. Financial Wellness:

- Budgeting and Financial Planning:
  - Establishing a budget and engaging in financial planning can contribute to a sense of control and reduce stress related to financial concerns.
    - Emergency Fund:

- Building an emergency fund provides a financial safety net, reducing anxiety about unexpected expenses.

Conclusion:

Prevention strategies for stress are multifaceted and involve adopting a holistic approach to overall well-being. Incorporating these strategies into daily life can contribute to resilience, better stress management, and improved overall mental and physical health. It's essential to recognize that prevention is an ongoing process, and individuals may need to adapt and refine their strategies based on changing circumstances and stressors.

Chapter 20

Global Perspectives on Stress

Global perspectives on stress vary significantly due to cultural, socioeconomic, and environmental factors. Stress is a universal experience, but its causes, manifestations, and coping mechanisms can differ across regions and populations. Here are some global perspectives on stress:

1. Cultural Influences:

- Collectivism vs. Individualism:
    - Cultures that emphasize collectivism may prioritize social harmony and group cohesion, influencing how individuals experience and cope with stress. In individualistic cultures, personal achievement and autonomy may play a more significant role.
- Coping Styles:
    - Cultural norms shape coping styles. Some cultures may encourage emotional expression and social support seeking, while others may emphasize stoicism or individual problem-solving.

2. Workplace Stress:

- High-Pressure Industries:
    - Certain industries, such as finance or technology, may be associated with high levels of stress globally due to demanding work environments and intense competition.
- Work-Life Balance:
    - Cultures vary in their approach to work-life balance. Some cultures prioritize long working hours, while others emphasize leisure and family time.

3. Economic Factors:

- Income Disparities:
    - Economic disparities contribute to stress. In regions with significant income inequality, individuals may face stress related to financial insecurity and limited access to resources.
- Global Economic Trends:
    - Global economic downturns, recessions, or financial crises can have widespread effects, influencing stress levels on a global scale.

4. Sociopolitical Context:

- Conflict and Instability:
    - Regions facing political instability, conflict, or social unrest may experience heightened stress levels among the population.
    - Migration and Displacement:
        - Individuals and communities affected by forced migration or displacement often encounter stressors related to uncertainty, loss, and adaptation to new environments.

5. Technology and Modernization:

- Technological Stress:
    - Rapid technological advancements and increased connectivity can contribute to stress, especially in societies where individuals feel pressure to constantly stay connected and updated.
    - Social Media Impact:
        - The impact of social media on stress varies globally. While it can enhance social connections, it may also contribute to stress through factors like online harassment and

social comparison.

6. Health and Well-Being:

- Access to Healthcare:
  - Disparities in healthcare access contribute to stress, with individuals in certain regions facing challenges in obtaining adequate medical care.
- Cultural Attitudes Toward Mental Health:
  - Stigma surrounding mental health can vary globally, affecting how individuals seek and receive support for stress-related issues.

7. Educational Systems:

- Academic Pressure:
  - Countries with highly competitive education systems may witness stress among students due to academic pressure and expectations.
    - Cultural Attitudes Toward Education:
      - Cultural values related to education influence stress levels. Some cultures prioritize academic achievement, while others emphasize a more holistic approach to learning.

8. Natural Disasters and Climate Change:

- Vulnerability to Disasters:
  - Regions prone to natural disasters may experience chronic stress due to the constant threat of environmental hazards.
    - Climate Change Impact:
      - Climate-related events, such as extreme weather conditions or rising sea levels,

contribute to stress, particularly in vulnerable communities.

9. Social Support Structures:

- Community and Family Support:
  - The strength of community and family support systems can influence how individuals cope with stress. Tight-knit communities may provide a buffer against stressors.
    - Isolation and Loneliness:
      - Societal trends toward increased individualization and urbanization may contribute to feelings of isolation and loneliness, impacting stress levels.

Milton Keynes UK
Ingram Content Group UK Ltd.
UKHW020754241123
433194UK00015B/868